NUFFIELD DESIGN & TECHNOLOGY

STUDY GUIDE

Longman Group Ltd
Longman House, Burnt Mill, Harlow,
Essex CM20 2JE
and associated companies throughout the world.

First published 1995
Third impression 1995
ISBN 0582 21265 0

Set in Garamond ITC Light Bt 12/13
Designed and produced by Gecko Ltd, Bicester, Oxon OX6 0JT.
Printed in Hong Kong
GC/03

The publisher's policy is to use paper manufactured from sustainable forests.

Project directors

Executive director Dr David Barlex (Goldsmiths' College, University of London)

Co-directors Prof. Paul Black (King's College, London) and Prof. Geoffrey Harrison (Nottingham Trent University)

Deputy director – dissemination David Wise (Windlesham House School)

Contributors

Part 1

David Barlex, Goldsmiths' College, University of London
Eileen Barlex, Design Council
Jo Compton, Institute of Education

Part 2

Eileen Barlex, Design Council
Catherine Budgett-Meakin, Intermediate Technology Group
Jo Compton, Institute of Education, University of London
Keith Everett, Education Consultant
David Fair, Education Television Producer
Ann Hampton, Intermediate Technology Group
Niel McLean, Ealing TVEI
Mike Martin, Intermediate Technology Group
Judith Powling, Design Council
Val Rea, Intermediate Technology Group

Early developments

Ian Fletcher, Warwickshire LEA
Ann Hepher, Kingston LEA
School of Education, University of Bath
South West Region School Technology Forum
North West Region of TVEI
Nottingham Technology Education Development Group, Nottingham Trent University
Nuffield Chelsea Curriculum Trust
United Biscuits Leicestershire Development Group

The Nuffield Design and Technology Project gratefully acknowledges the support of the following commercial concerns in developing the published materials:
GEC Education Liaison
Zeneca Pharmaceuticals (formerly ICI Pharmaceuticals)
Tesco Training & Education Department
United Biscuits UK Ltd

Project manager Diona Gregory

Editors Katie Chester, Helen Johnson, Bettina Wilkes

Picture researcher Louise Edgeworth

Indexer Richard Raper/Indexing Specialists

Illustrations by Gecko Ltd, John Plumb and Martin Sanders

Safety
Longman Education is grateful to Martin Trevor for advice on safety matters. Every effort has been taken to ensure safe practice.

Contents

Part 1

Part 2 Case Studies

1 Welcome to design and technology

What do you do in design and technology?

How does this book help?

This is *not* a text book. You don't work your way through it bit by bit each week or sit and read it all in one go.

You use this book to help you to get better and better at design and technology.

Sometimes you will use the book on your own.

Sometimes your teacher will ask you to look at one part of the book.

Sometimes you will need to look at it with friends.

Doing design and technology

Resource Tasks for learning knowledge, skills and understanding

It is difficult to design and make well if you have not got much knowledge or skill. We use **Resource Tasks** to teach you what you need to know. These are short practical activities. You will find them amusing and puzzling and they will really help you to learn. You will be given a Resource Task as an instruction sheet like this one. They are always laid out in the same way.

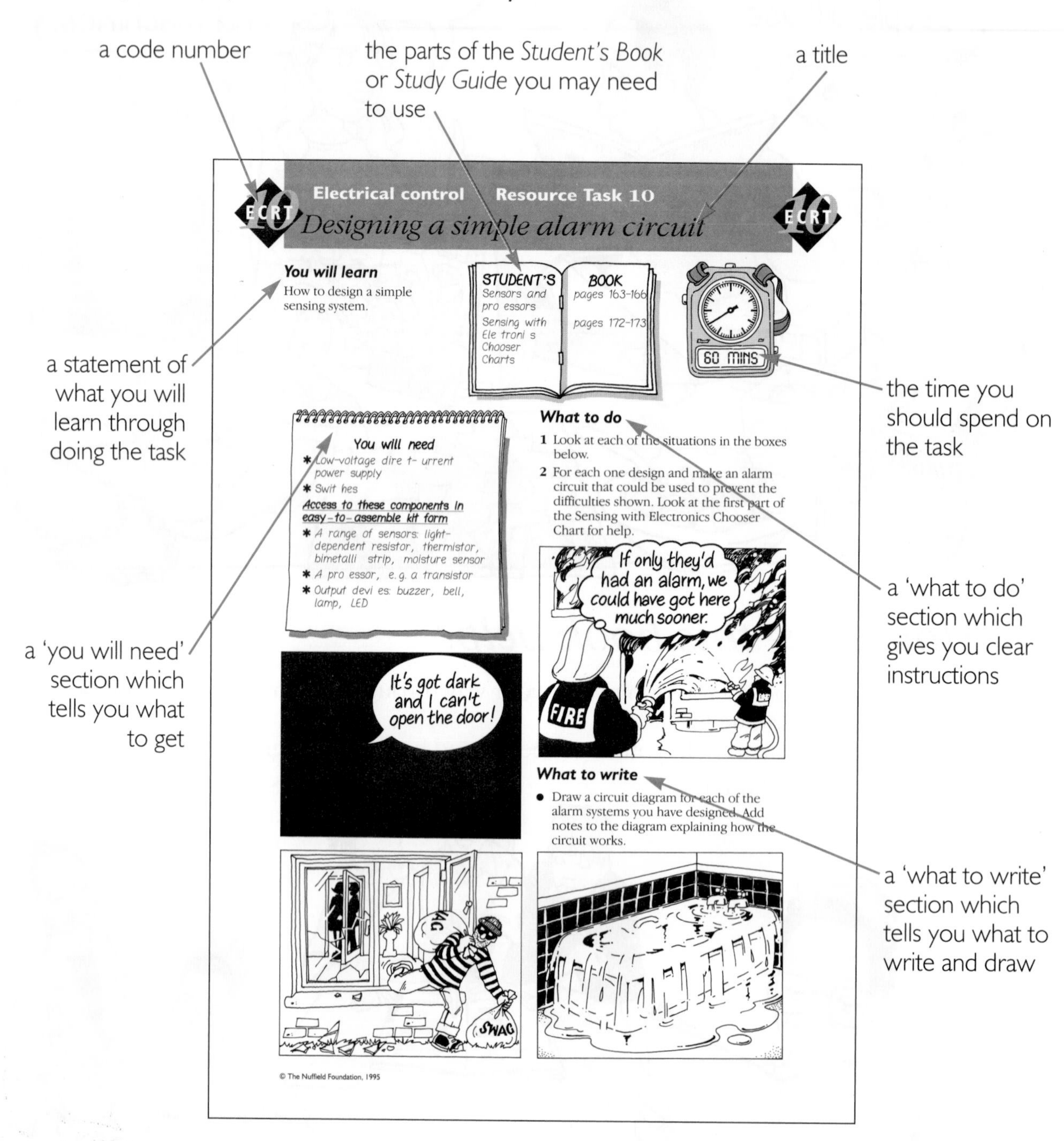

ECRT 10

Electrical control Resource Task 10

Designing a simple alarm circuit

You will learn

How to design a simple sensing system.

STUDENT'S BOOK
Sensors and pro essors — pages 163–166
Sensing with Ele troni s Chooser Charts — pages 172–173

60 MINS

You will need

* Low-voltage dire t- urrent power supply
* Swit hes

Access to these components in easy-to-assemble kit form

* A range of sensors: light-dependent resistor, thermistor, bimetalli strip, moisture sensor
* A pro essor, e.g. a transistor
* Output devi es: buzzer, bell, lamp, LED

What to do

1. Look at each of the situations in the boxes below.
2. For each one design and make an alarm circuit that could be used to prevent the difficulties shown. Look at the first part of the Sensing with Electronics Chooser Chart for help.

What to write

- Draw a circuit diagram for each of the alarm systems you have designed. Add notes to the diagram explaining how the circuit works.

Learning about the design and technology of others

The second part of this book contains **Case Studies**. These are true stories about how people, at different times in history and in different parts of the world, have used their skills in design and technology to meet their needs. By reading the Case Studies you will learn things that help you get better at designing and making.

Each Case Study is a story with pictures, and includes three sorts of activities, to help you understand and learn from the Case Study. The examples on this page tell you more about these activities.

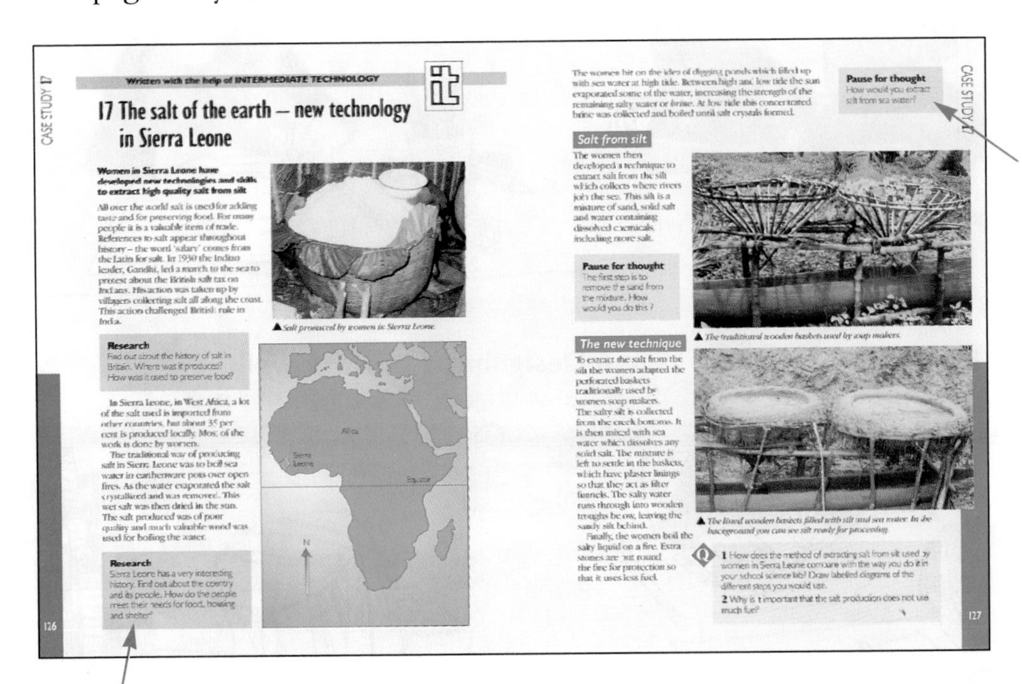

Pause for thought – Here you are asked questions to help you think about what you have just read so that the next bit makes more sense. You don't have to write anything down.

Research – This asks you to find out more and write about what you have found out. You may need to use the library or talk to an expert. You will probably need to do this as homework.

Q Here you should stop reading and tackle the question. You may need to write down an answer, make a drawing or a model, discuss the Case Study with a friend or make a short presentation to the class.

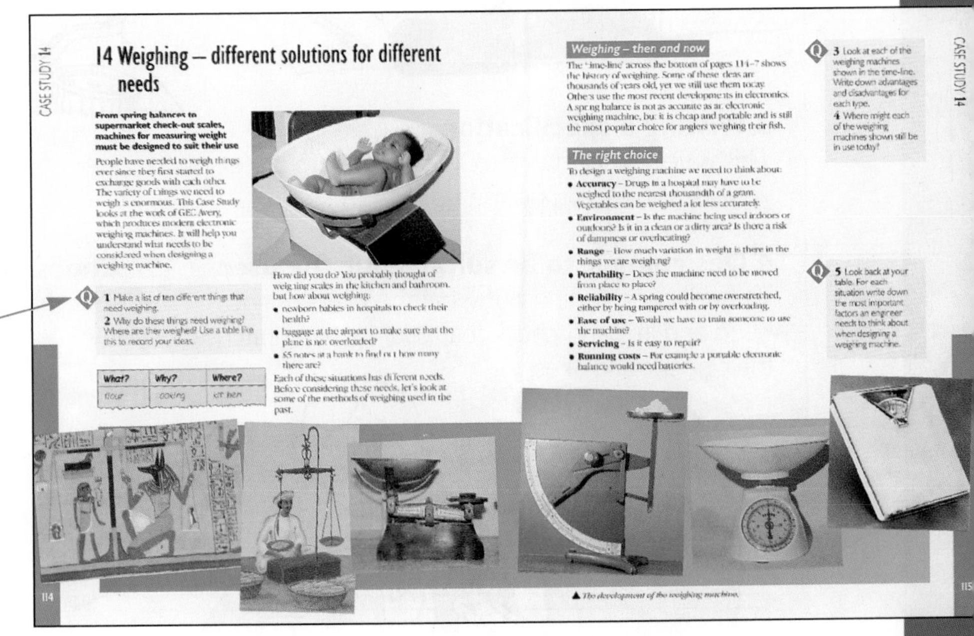

Capability Tasks for designing and making

In a **Capability Task** you have to design and make a real product that works. This is what you do.

1 Starting off

Your teacher will talk to the class about the sort of thing you might design and make.

You will have to find out what the people who will use your product might need and like.

2 Writing a design brief

Write one sentence describing the sort of thing you will make, what it is for and who will use it.

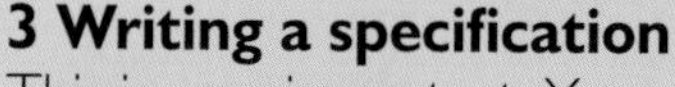

3 Writing a specification

This is very important. You will need it to check on your design as you do the task.

4 Designing it to be suitable for the user

You will need to find out what the users might need and like and check that your design matches their needs and likes.

5 Designing it to look right

Write and draw what your design could look like. You may need to make models and collect samples as well.

6 Designing it to work well

Use writing and drawing to show how your design will work. Use working models and samples to get the details right.

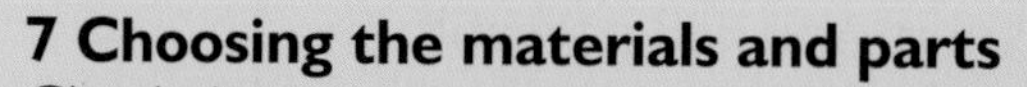

7 Choosing the materials and parts

Check that you can get the materials and parts that you need.

8 Choosing the tools and equipment
Make sure you know how to use them properly.

9 Planning the making
Work out the main steps and check that you have enough time.

10 Doing the making
Don't rush. Make sure you don't lose any parts.

11 Altering your design
While you are making your product, you may think of ways of making your design better. If you do, write down *how* they will make it better *and* check that your changed design still meets the specification.

12 Evaluating your product
Test your final product to find out just how good it is.

13 Presenting your work
You may have to tell the story of your designing and making:

- where the ideas came from;
- how they developed;
- how you made it;
- how good it was.

3 What you need to learn about

Finding out about needs and wants

The products that you make in your design and technology lessons should meet the **needs** and **wants** of the people who will use them. You can find out what people might need or want by talking to them and seeing how they live and work. You can find out more about people's needs and wants by reading Chapter 1 of the *Student's Book*.

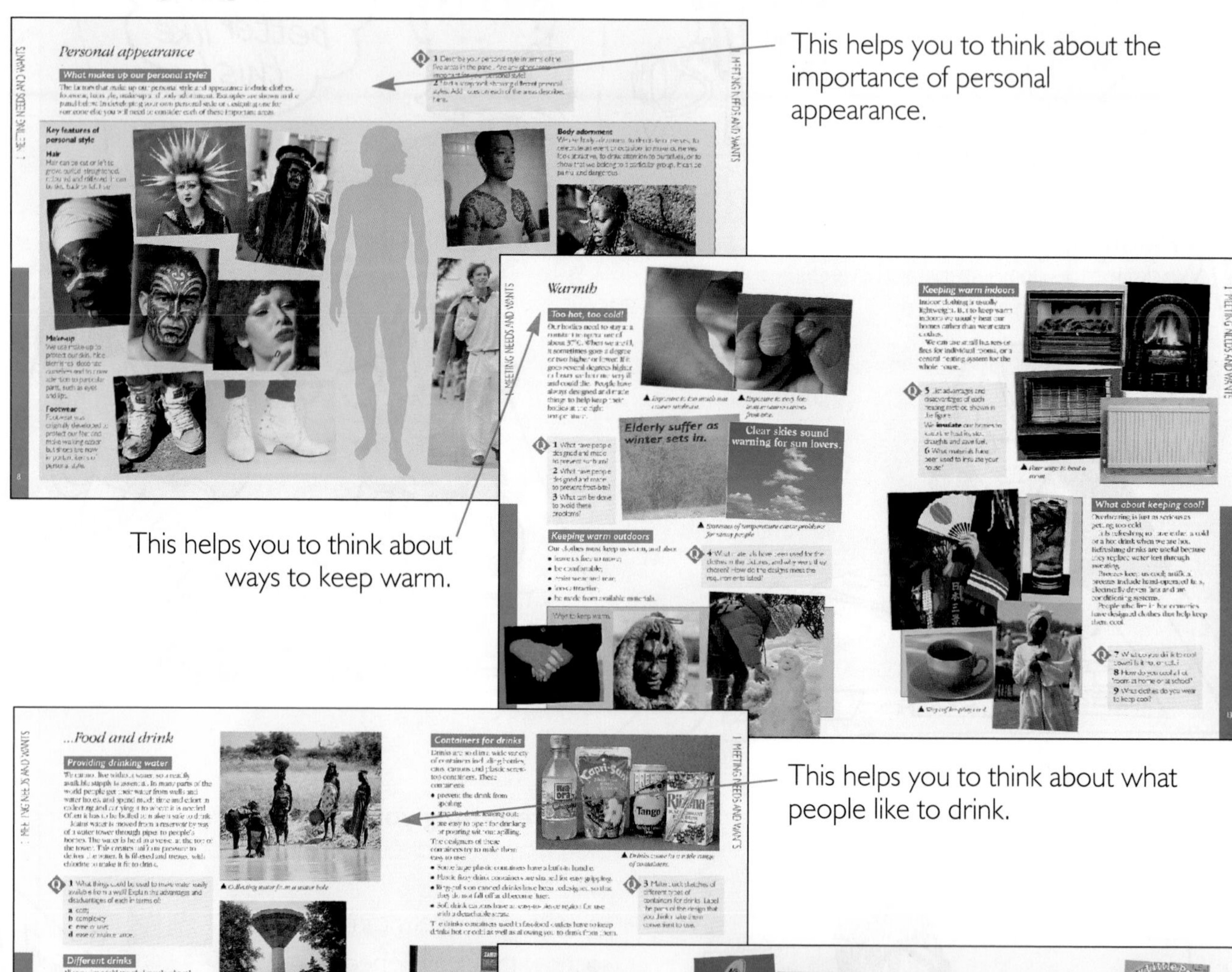

This helps you to think about the importance of personal appearance.

This helps you to think about ways to keep warm.

This helps you to think about what people like to drink.

This helps you to think about ways people use leisure time.

Learning to use strategies

Each big design and make task, or Capability Task, is made up of lots of smaller tasks. There are different ways of doing these tasks – these are called **strategies**. To be successful in designing and making you have to choose the right strategy.

Chapter 2 of the *Student's Book* describes the strategies you will need to be successful in all the small tasks that make up a Capability Task.

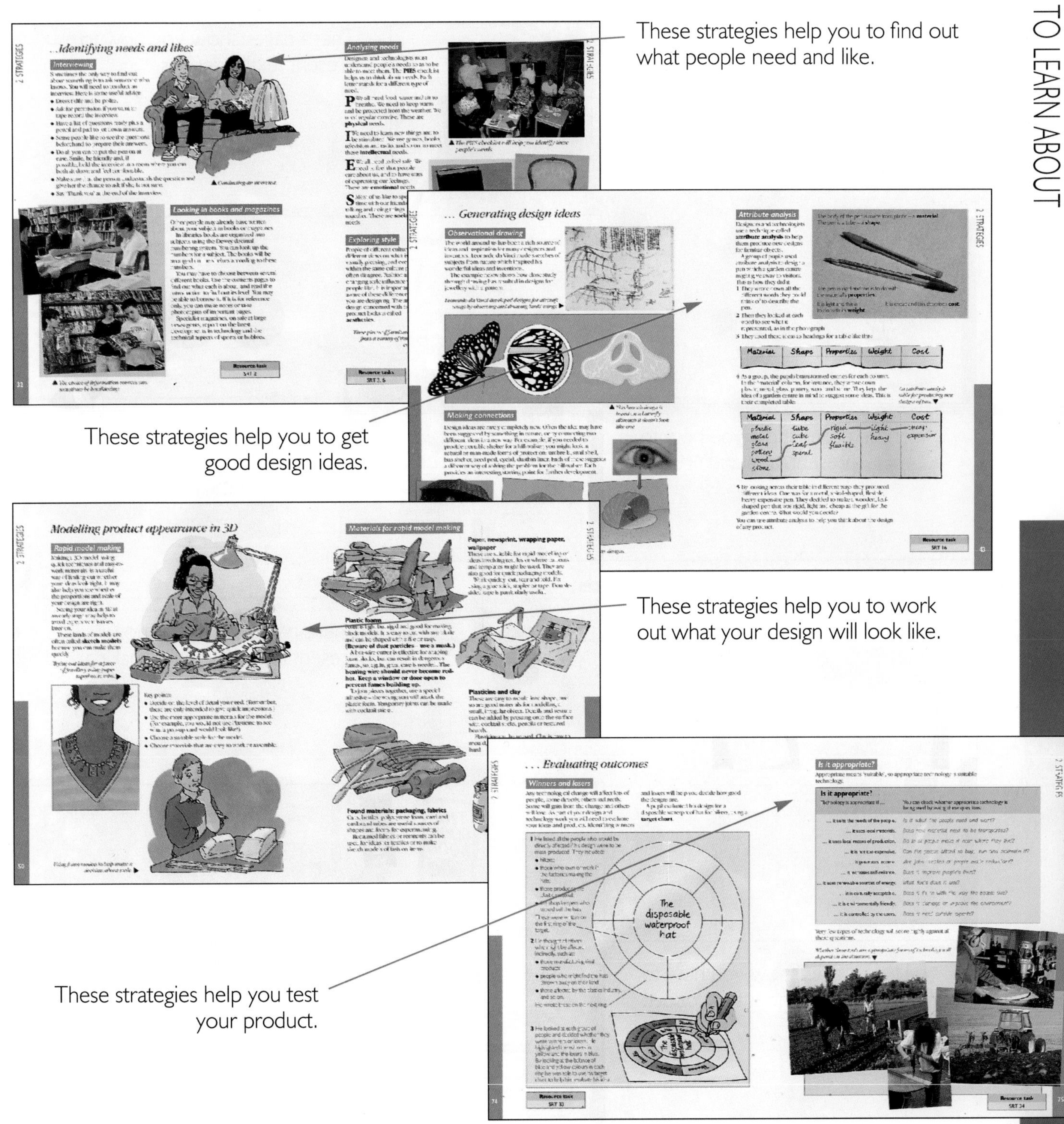

Communicating your ideas

You need to be able to explain your design ideas to other people – to **communicate** or **present** them. There are different ways of doing this. The way you choose will depend on who the other people are and why they need to know.

Chapter 3 of the *Student's Book* describes how you can communicate your design ideas.

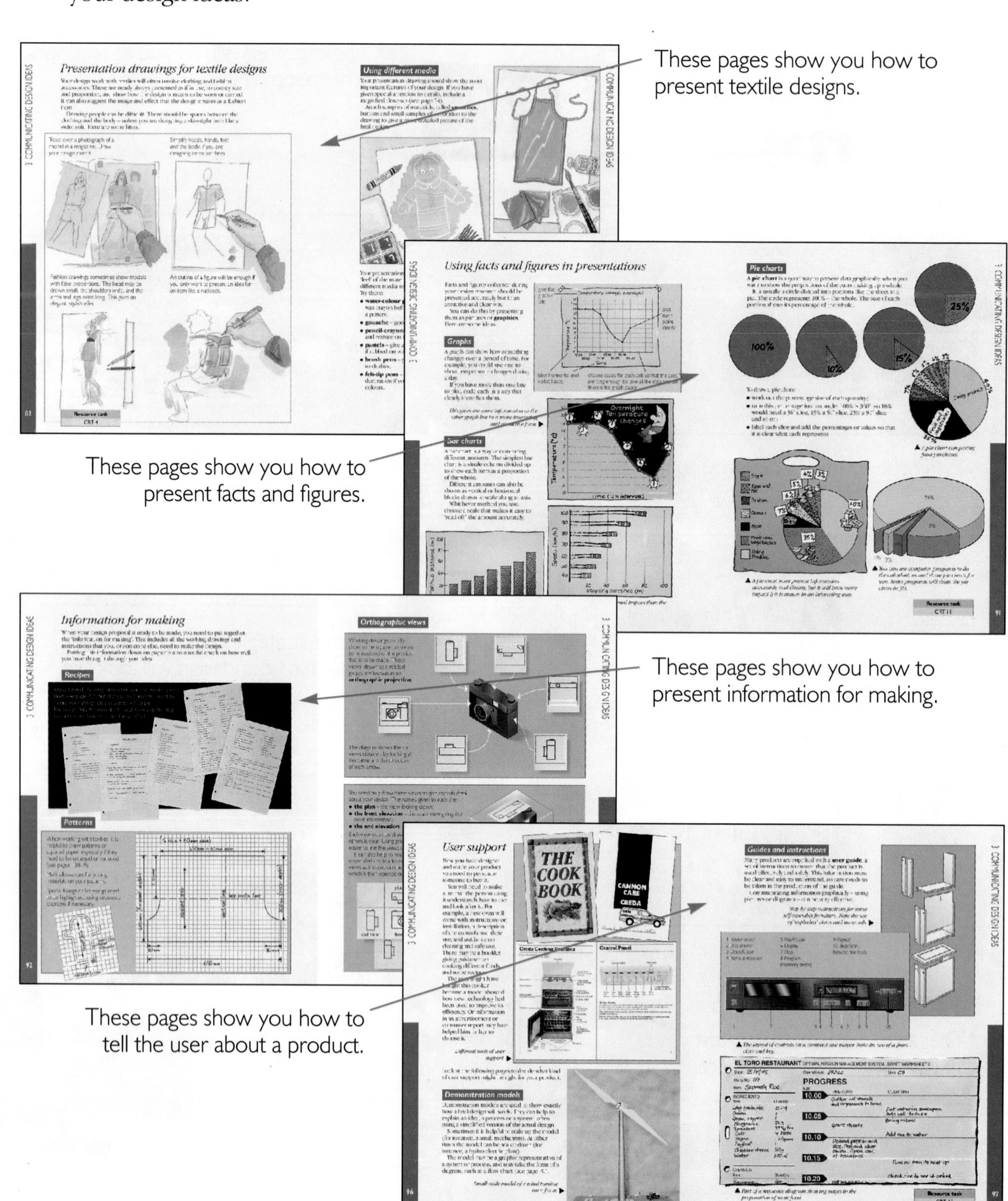

Learning to design and make with food

To design and make food products you need to know:

- about when, how and what people eat, and about nutrition;
- about food materials – what they are like, how to cook with them and their nutritional value;
- how to keep or preserve food so that it is fit to eat.

Chapter 11 of the *Student's Book* tells you what you need to know to design and make with food.

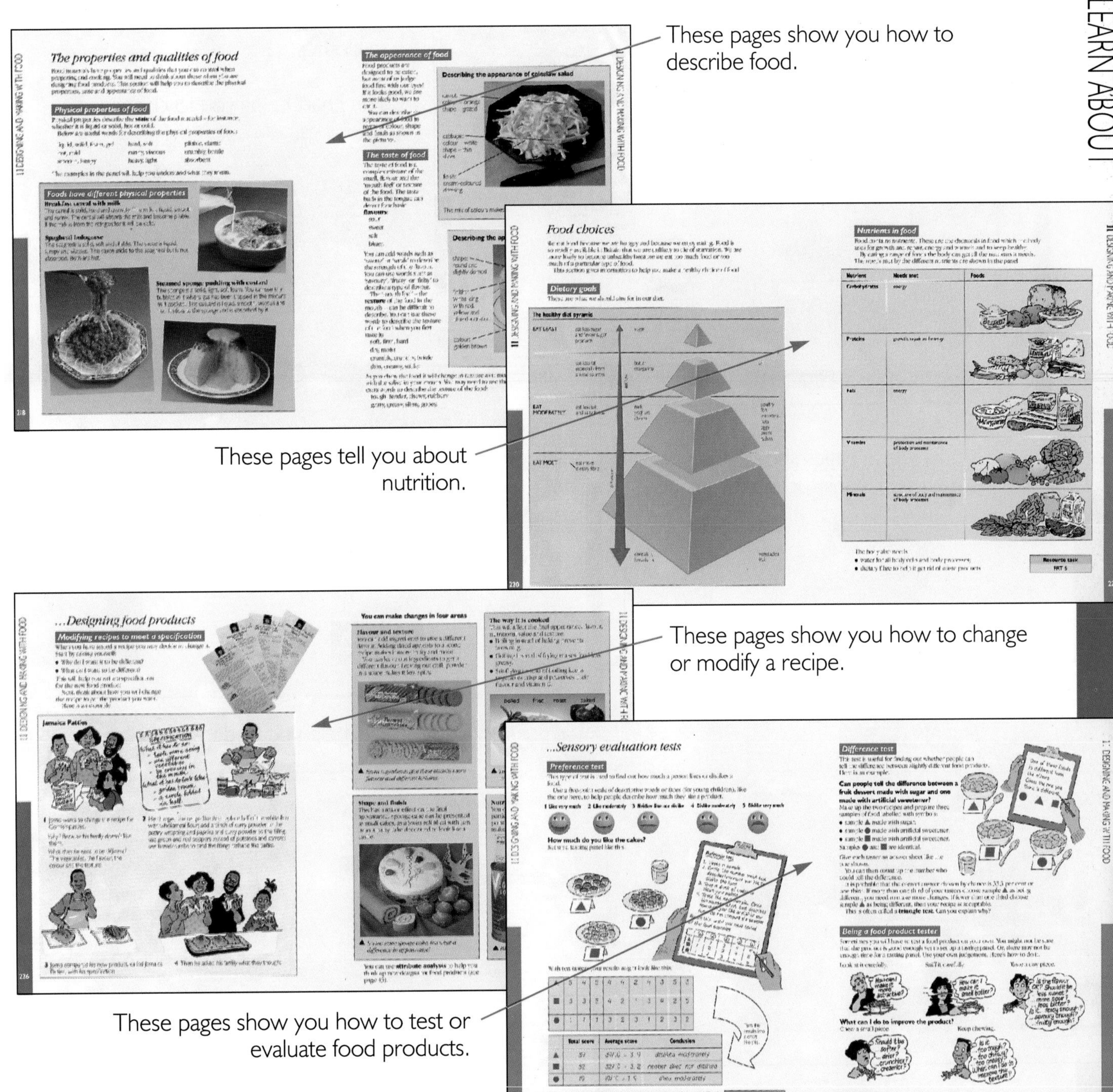

Learning to design and make with textiles

To design and make textile products you need to know:

- about the properties of textile materials so that you can choose the right fabric;
- how to draft and cut patterns;
- how to join fabrics;
- how to decorate fabrics.

You can find out about these and much more in Chapter 5 of the *Student's Book*.

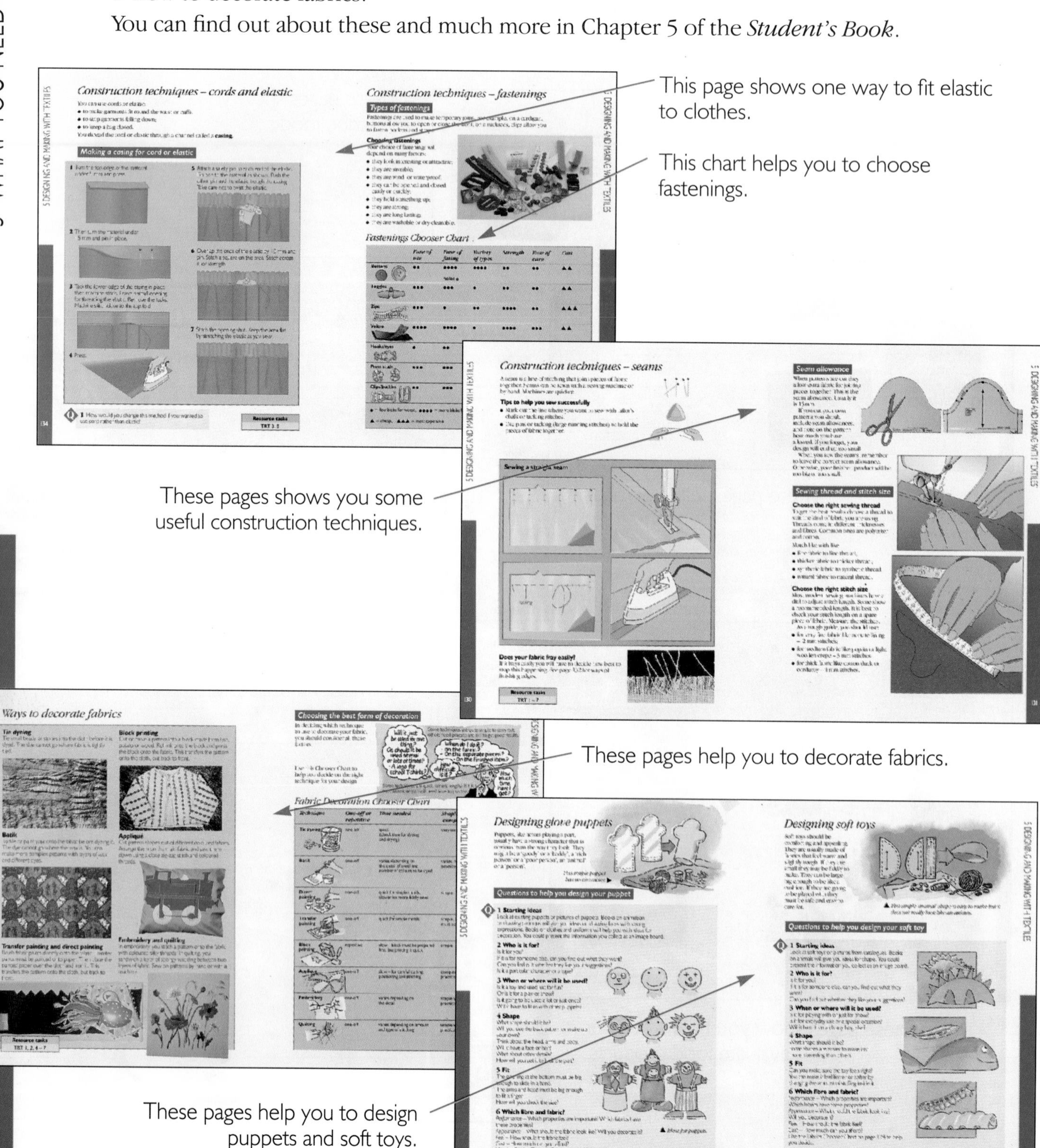

Learning to design and make with resistant materials

To design and make products from **resistant materials** – wood, metal and plastics – you need to know:

- about the properties of the materials so that you can choose the ones that are right for your product;
- how to choose and use the right tools and equipment to cut and shape materials for your design;
- how to make these materials look good.

Chapter 10 of the *Student's Book* describes what you need to know to work with resistant materials.

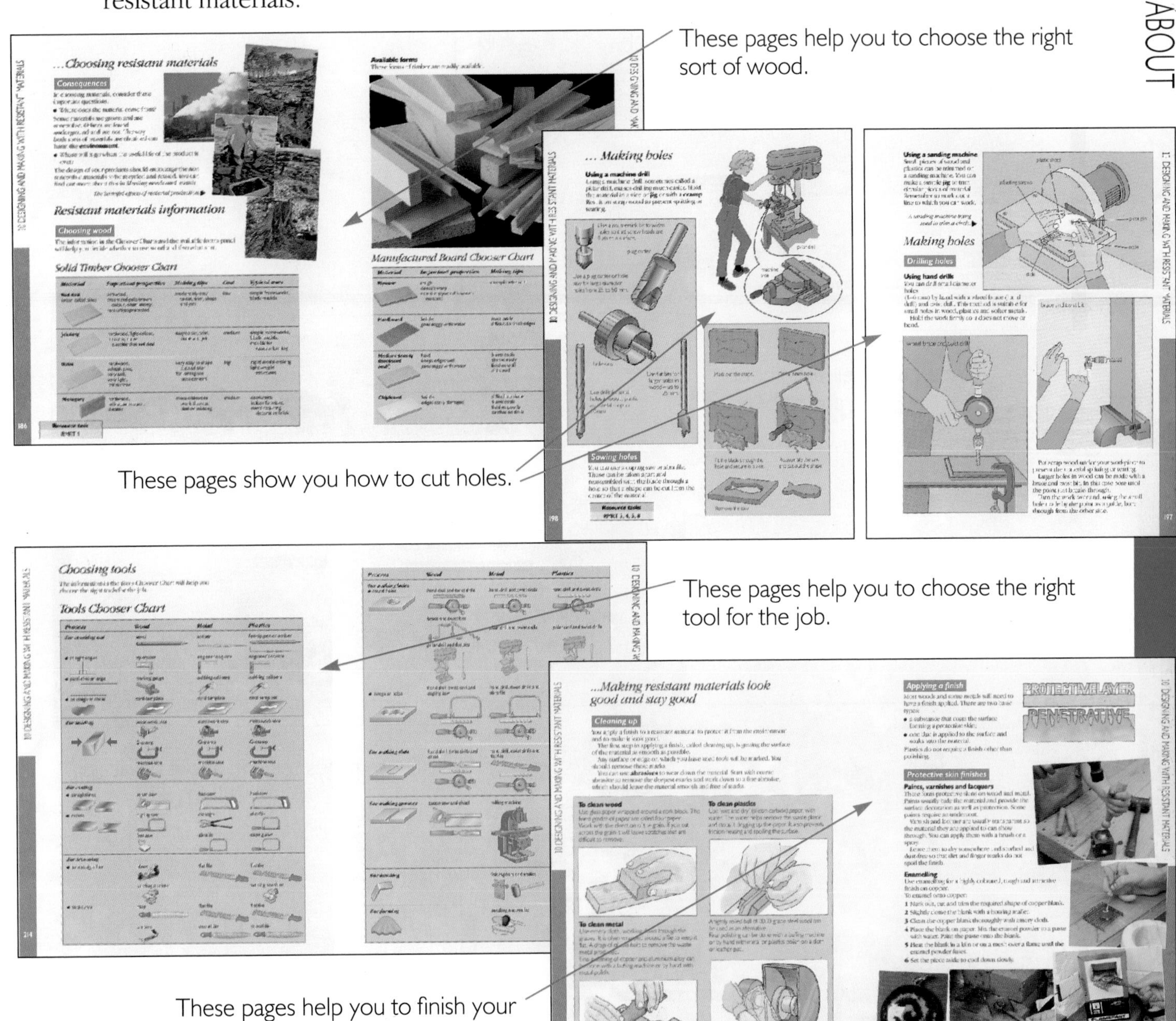

Learning to design and make with structures

All the products you design and make will have a **structure** that will have to be able to stand up to different forces. You need to know about the way structures work, so that your products do not break or bend too much.

Chapter 9 of the *Student's Book* explains how six different types of structure work.

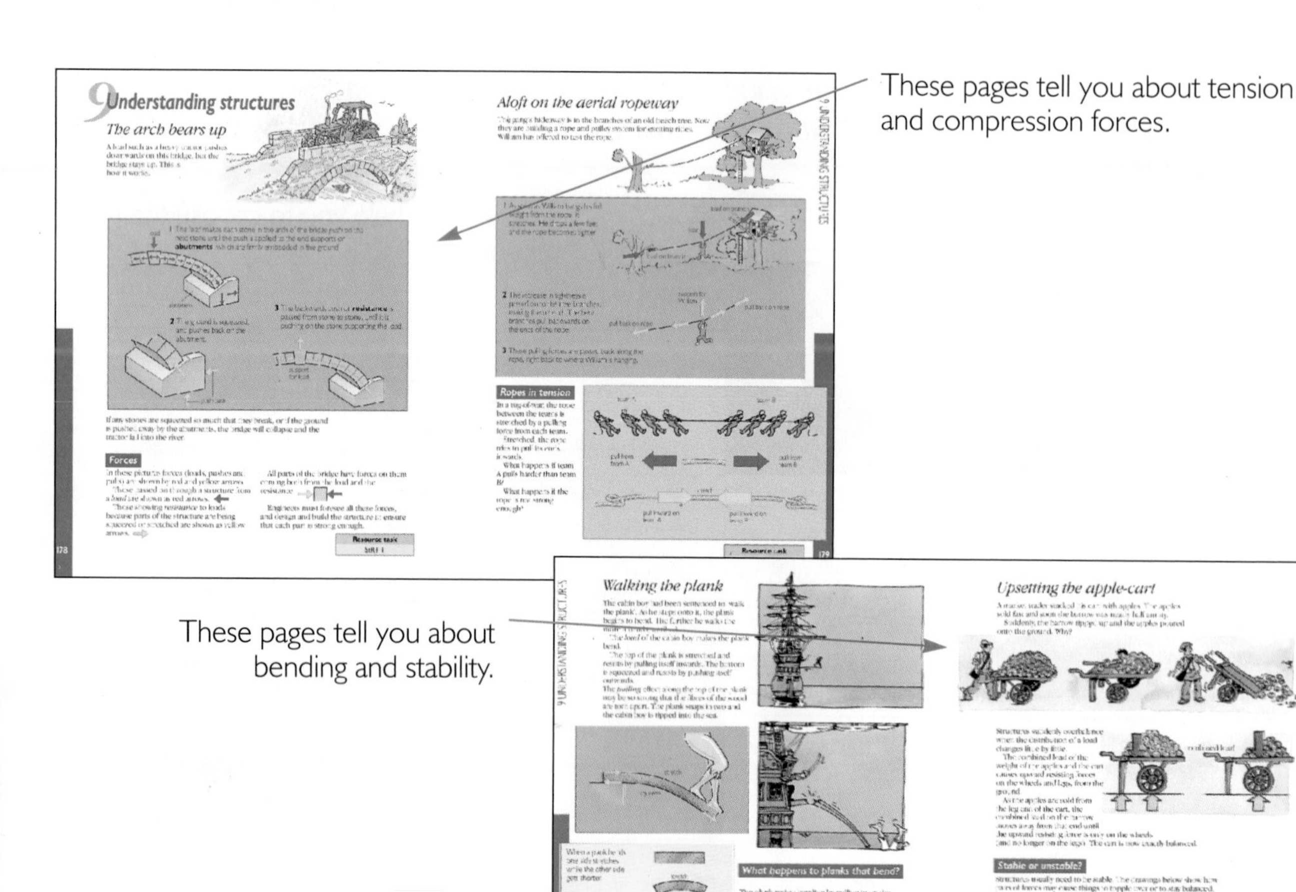

These pages tell you about tension and compression forces.

These pages tell you about bending and stability.

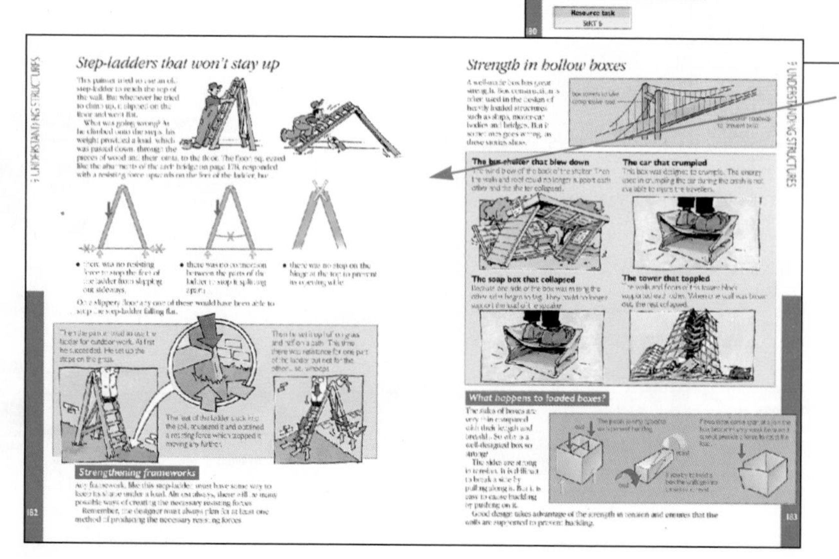

These pages tell you about collapsing.

Learning to design and make with mechanisms

If you design a product with moving parts it must have a **mechanism**. To design mechanisms successfully you need to:

- know what they can do and which ones will do it best for your product;
- work accurately so that the moving parts of your product are reliable and work well.

Chapter 4 of the *Student's Book* is all about mechanisms.

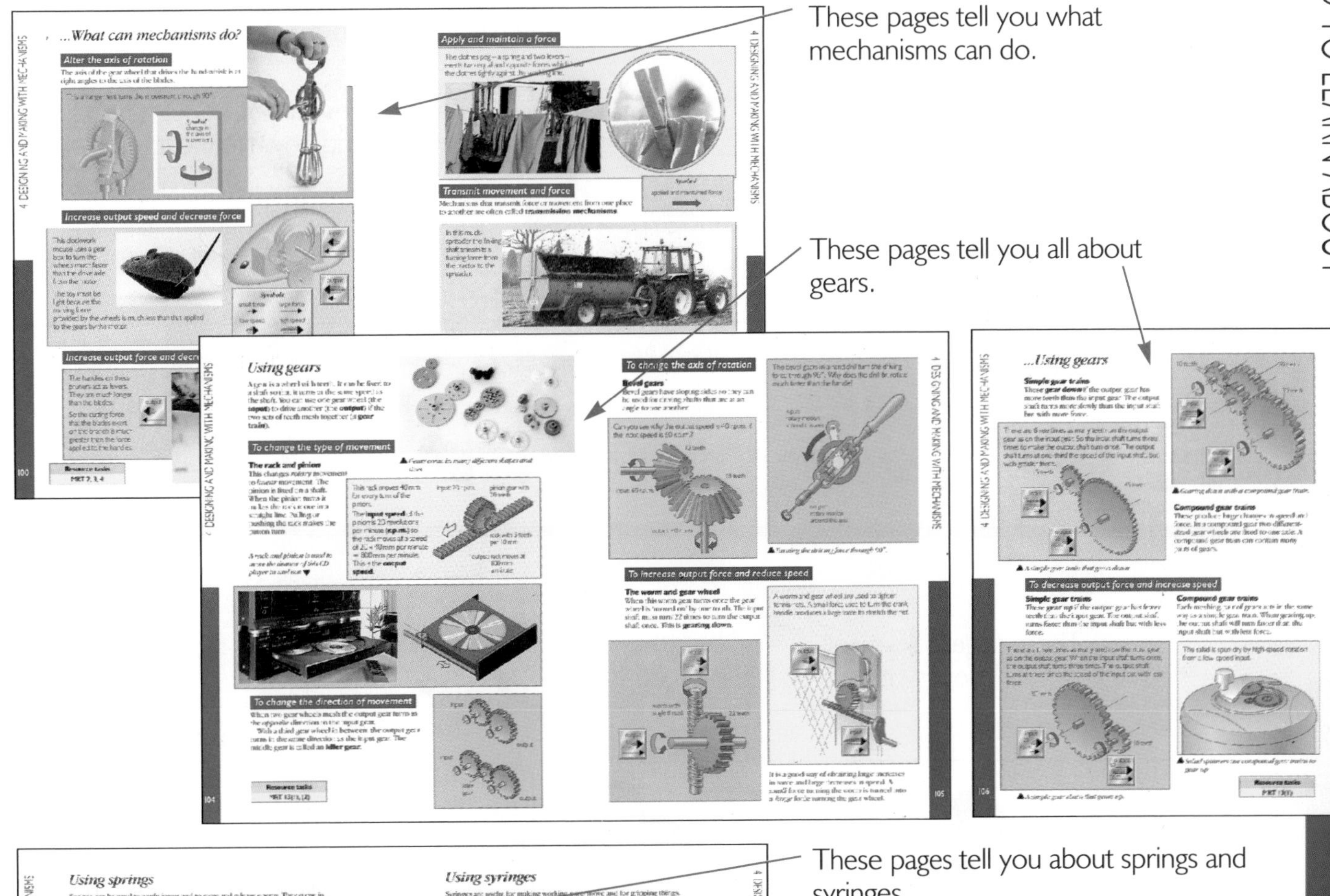

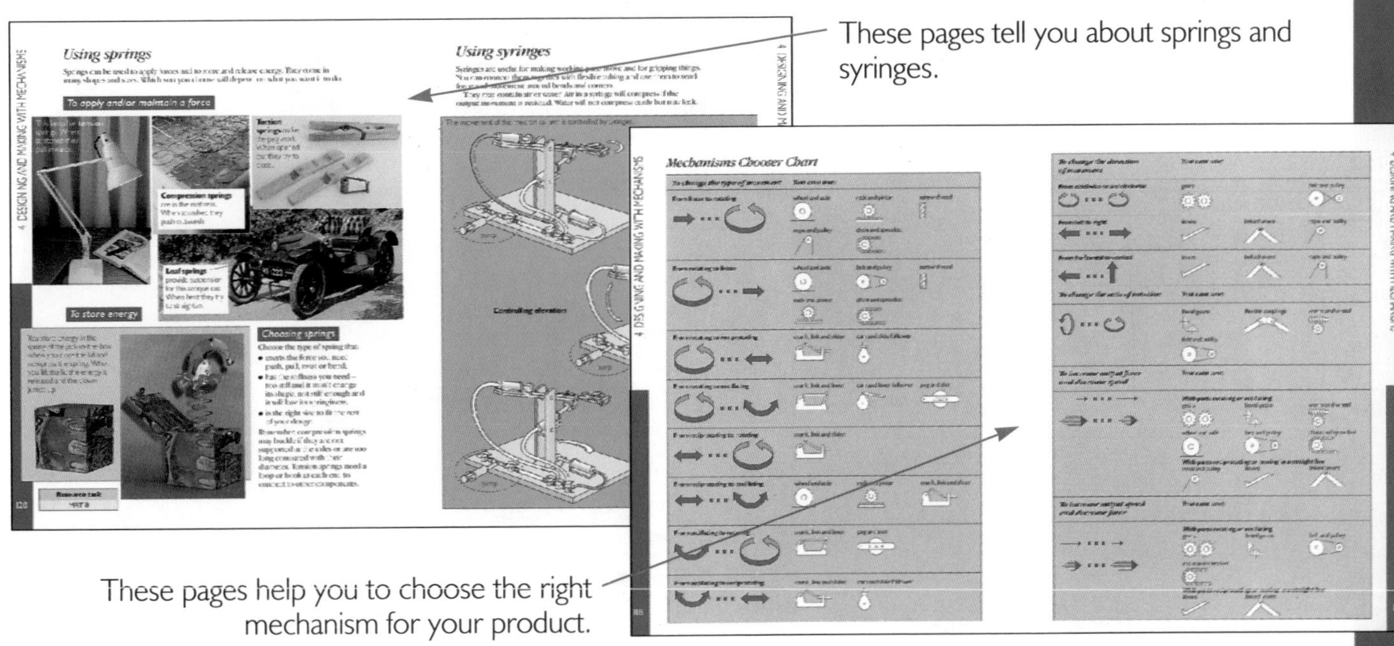

Learning to design and make with electric circuits

If you design a product with an electric motor or lights you need to use an **electric circuit**. To design an electric circuit you need to know:

- about different electrical parts or **components** and what they can do;
- how to connect components so that they form a circuit that does what you want.

Chapter 6 of the *Student's Book* is all about using electrical components to design circuits.

Learning to design and make with electronic circuits

You may design a product that includes an **electronic circuit**. These can be complicated, but using a **systems approach** will help you get the electronic part right.

You have to think about:

- the inputs and the outputs;
- what you need to turn the inputs into outputs – the processor.

You need to know about:

- electronic components and what they can do;
- how to connect the components together so that they form a circuit that does what you want;
- how to make your product easy to use and look good.

Chapter 7 of the *Student's Book* describes what you need to know about designing and making electronic products.

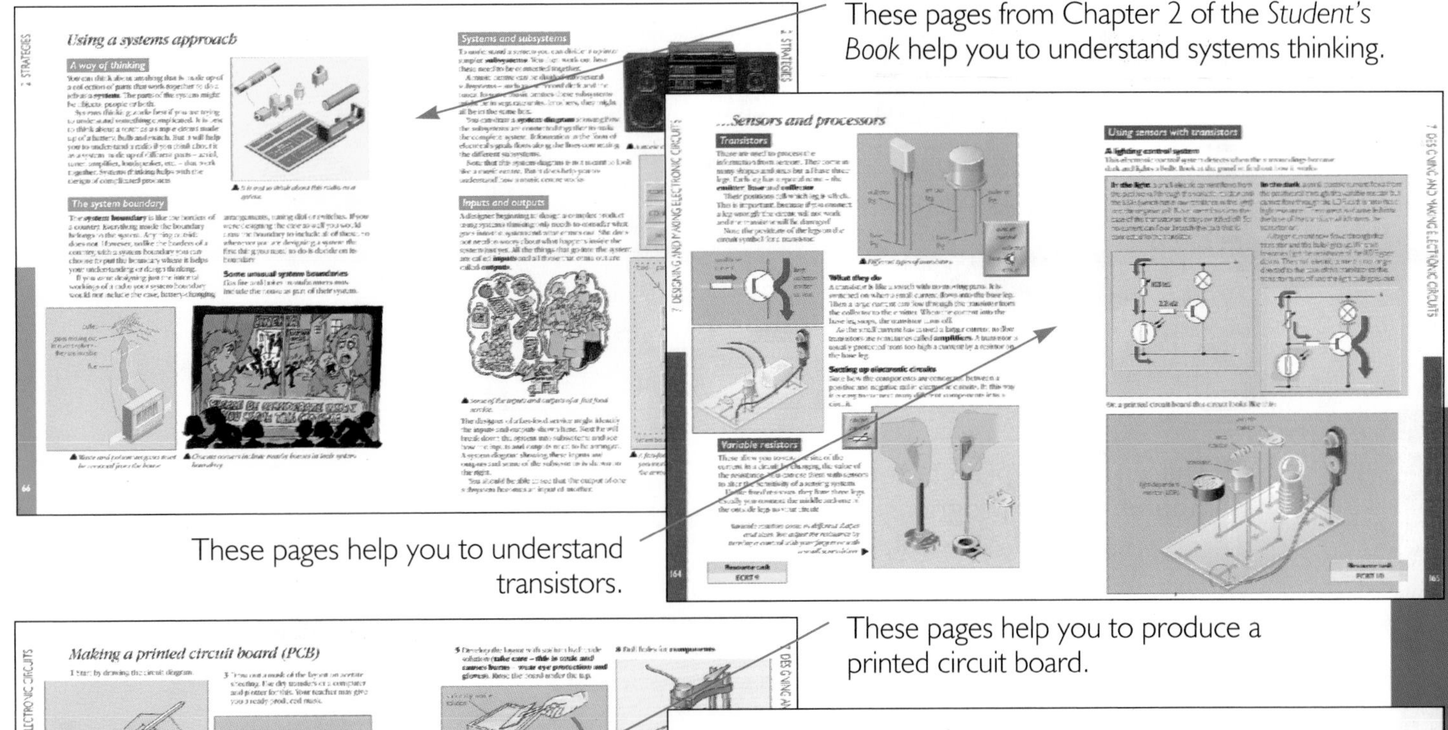

These pages from Chapter 2 of the *Student's Book* help you to understand systems thinking.

These pages help you to understand transistors.

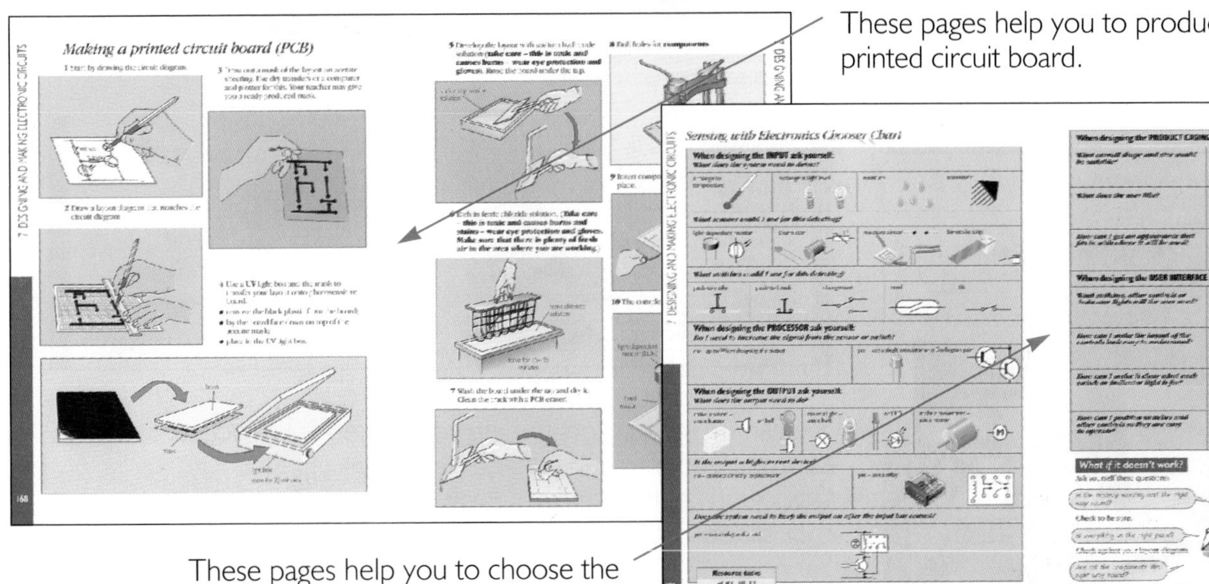

These pages help you to produce a printed circuit board.

These pages help you to choose the right electronic components and get the overall design of the product right.

Learning to design and make with computer control

Sometimes you will design and make a product that can be controlled by a **computer**. The product might be made from a construction kit or you might have made some of the parts yourself. You can't connect your product directly to a computer. You need to connect it to an **interface box** which is then connected to the computer. You need to know:

- how to write instructions for the computer so that it can tell your product what to do. This is called **programming**.

You can find out how to do this in Chapter 8 of the *Student's Book*.

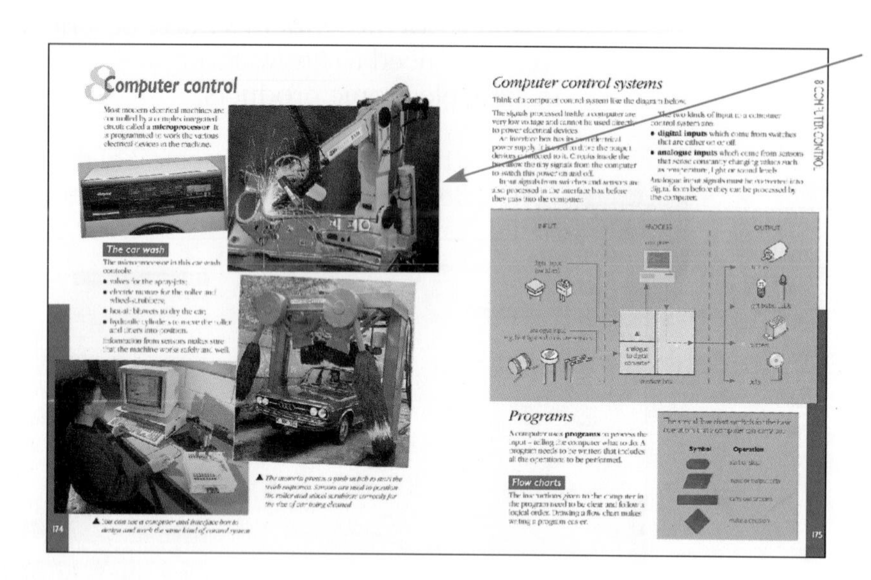

8 Computer control

The car wash

Computer control systems

Programs

Flow charts

These pages help you to use computer control.

These pages explain how computer control programs work.

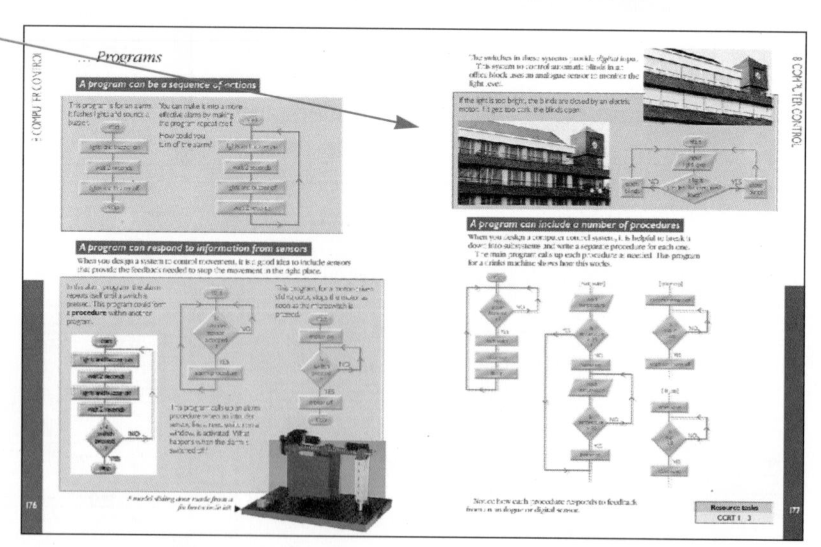

Programs

A program can be a sequence of actions

A program can respond to information from sensors

A program can include a number of procedures

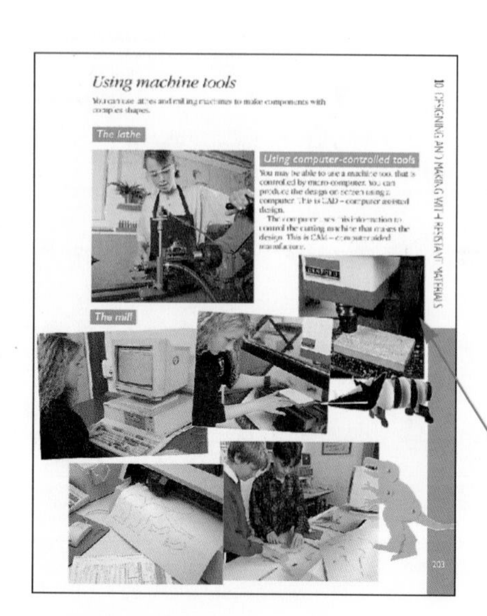

Using machine tools

The lathe

Using computer-controlled tools

The mill

You can use computers to help you make your products by using a computer-controlled machine tool.
Chapter 10 of the *Student's Book* gives some examples.
Your school may have equipment like this.

4 A closer look at Capability Tasks

Exploring user needs and wants

When you are designing and making you need to find out what the user of the product might need or want. There are several ways to do this. As you get better at design and technology you will be able to choose how to do this for yourself. To begin with your teacher will help. Here are some possible ways:

▲ *You can discuss needs and wants in a small group.*

▲ *You can use the PIES method to explore needs and wants.*

What's in it for you?

If you understand what people need and want, the products you design and make will be very successful.

▲ *The whole class can talk about what the needs and wants might be.*

▲ *You can talk to the people who might use the product.*

▲ *You can watch what people do.*

Deciding exactly what to design and make

Writing a design brief

It is always important to be clear about what you are trying to produce when you tackle a designing and making task. One way to do this is to write a **design brief**. To begin with you will do this as a whole class. As you get better you will work it out on your own. You should write down:

- the sort of thing you want to make;
- who it is for;
- where it will be used.

▲ *The whole class can help to work out the design brief.*

Writing a specification

Once you have a design brief it is important to develop a **specification** for your product. This will tell you:

- what the product has to do;
- what it should look like;
- any other important details such as the materials or components to be used.

You must write a specification for the product you are going to design and make. It is impossible to be successful without one!

▲ *You can discuss the details of a design brief before you write it down.*

▲ *Everyone should take part in working out the specification.*

What's in it for you?

If you write a good design brief it will help you get lots of different, useful design ideas. If you write a good specification you will be able to develop these ideas into a product that works well and looks good.

▲ *You must write a specification.*

Getting design ideas

There are lots of ways to do this. Sometimes it is important to work in a group and share ideas. At other times you need to work on your own.

▲ *Brainstorming is a good way to get lots of ideas.*

▲ *Drawing from nature can give you ideas.*

What's in it for you?

If you learn how to use these ways of getting ideas, you will never have to say 'But I can't think of anything!' again.

▲ *You can get interesting designs by putting different ideas together.*

ATTRIBUTE ANALYSIS – FELT TIP PENS

Size	small	jumbo
Shape	thin tube	wide tube
Material	metal	plastic
Colour	silver barrel coloured cap	red barrel white cap
How it writes	thin lines	thick lines
Cost	expensive	cheap
Style	sleek	chunky

▲ *By describing existing products you can come up with new ideas.*

Developing your design ideas

Developing your design ideas

You will need to work out the details of your design ideas. There are lots of ways to do this. Some are shown here. To begin with your teacher will tell you what to do, but as you get better you will be able to choose for yourself.

▲ *Sketches with notes will help you to develop ideas.*

▲ *Make quick models to develop ideas.*

▲ *Make working models to get the technical details right.*

▲ *Quick tasting tests will help develop food product ideas.*

What's in it for you?

If you develop your ideas carefully you will find that the product you make will work well and look good.

Communicating your design ideas

You will need to show other people your design ideas. There are different ways to do this. The method you use will depend on why they want the information.

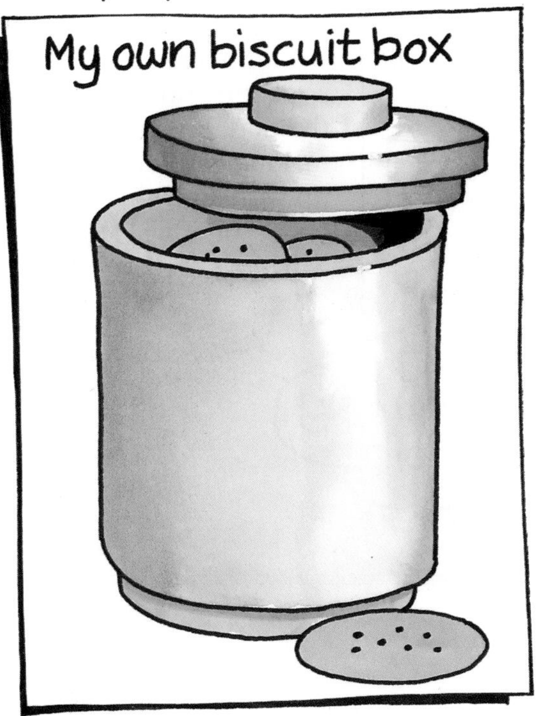

▲ *This presentation drawing shows just how attractive the biscuit box will be.*

▲ *This presentation drawing shows what the hat will look like and the materials that will be used.*

▲ *Clear graphics make this food product attractive.*

▲ *The drawing on the screen gives the information needed to make the biscuit box.*

What's in it for you?

If you present your design ideas well you will find that people will be interested in what you are designing and making and will want to use the product.

Planning and making

The making part of your designing and making is the time when you have to work most on your own. You need to plan what you are going to do so that it fits into the time available.

What's in it for you?

If you plan well you will have enough time to get your work finished and you won't spoil it by hurrying towards the end. If you do the making carefully you will end up with a product you can be proud of; it will look good and work well.

◀ *Use a flow chart to help you get it done on time.*

▲ *Whatever the material there is always plenty to do!*

Evaluating

You **evaluate** your product to find out how successful you have been at meeting the design brief and specification. Several ways to evaluate are shown here:

▲ *It is always important to test against the specification.*

▲ *It can sometimes be tough watching people use a product you have designed and made.*

▲ *Is it appropriate? It is not always easy to decide!*

▲ *When you are discussing winners and losers feelings can run high.*

- Some methods look at how well the product does its job and how easy it is to use;
- other methods look at how the product affects other people and the world around them.

What's in it for you?

If you learn to evaluate well, the quality of the products you design and make will get better because you won't make the same mistakes again.

5 Reviewing your work

What is a review?

A **review** is a time when you stop what you are doing and think about three things:

- what you have done;
- how well you have done it;
- what you should do next.

What's in it for you?

Reviewing helps you in three ways:

- It puts you in control. When you tackle a Capability Task you are in charge of your work. So you need to be clear about what you should do. Reviewing makes you stop and look at what you have done and how well you have done it. This affects what you should do next.
- It forces you to make decisions about what to do next and keeps you going. It is very easy to lose a sense of direction and waste time if you don't review your work.
- It can tell your teachers how well you are doing so that they can give you the help you need.

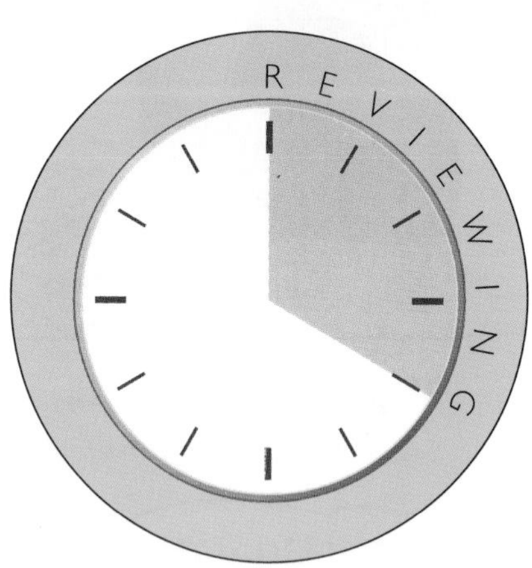

▲ *For reviewing – 20 minutes max!*

How long should it take?

Don't spend too long on reviewing. It should not take up so much time that you can't finish your work. A single review should not take more than 15 – 20 minutes.

How do you do it?

There are three main ways to review your work:

- **By talking to other students and your teacher** – This is a good way because it is quick and you can help each other by making suggestions. It is easy to forget what has been said if you don't write anything down.

- **By writing down your thoughts in a review diary** – This is a good way because you produce a record of your decisions which you can discuss with your teacher. It is important that it is not too long as this makes it difficult to use quickly when you are talking to your teacher.

- **By writing down answers to questions on a worksheet** – This is good because you are answering definite questions that are important. It is quite difficult to write a set of questions that is right for everyone's work. So you have to work out how each question relates to what you are doing.

When do you do it?

There are three points in a Capability Task when reviewing is particularly important.

Review 1
In the early stages of the task you will reach a point where you have a sketch of what you are going to design and make, and maybe a few notes about it. This is sometimes called your **design proposal** because it is what you propose to make. It is important to review this against the specification.

You need to ask questions like the ones opposite. By asking these sorts of questions you can make sure that your designing is getting off to a good start.

Review 2
Further on in the task you will reach a point when you have clear labelled drawings and notes describing your design and how you are going to make it. Now you need to review to check on two things:

It is important to ask this again as sometimes in developing your first ideas you can get carried away and lose sight of what the design has to do.

You need to check on materials, tools and equipment and to be sure that you have enough time.

Review 3
Once you have made your design you need to evaluate it.
You can ask any of these questions:

Or, take a **user trip** – try it out yourself, as someone who might buy it.

Understanding what keeps you back!

You can use a grid like this to work out what keeps you back and what you can do about it. Try filling it in when you have just finished a Capability Task. You can use notes, drawings or stickers. Have it with you when you talk to your teacher about getting better at design and technology.

STOP! What held me up?	**GO!** How did I overcome it?
HELP! When did I need it?	**YES!** How did I get it?
BORING! When do I lose interest?	**ENJOY!** How do I get it back?

Looking in detail at how you did

When you have just finished a Capability Task it is useful to stand back and look coldly at what you did and ask yourself three main questions:

- Was I clear about what I had to do?
- Did I use my time well?
- Did I get on with it?

You can use a grid like this to help you think about your work:

	Yes	No	Comments
Being clear			
Did I know what I was going to design and make?			
Did I know who it was for?			
Did I find out about their needs and wants?			
Did I write a specification?			
Did I learn what I needed to know through Resource Tasks and Case Studies?			
Using your time well			
Did I know how many lessons there were for the task?			
Did I have a time plan for what I had to do?			
Did I use homework time and school work time for the right things?			
Did I know when I had to start making in order to finish on time?			
Did I check that the materials, tools and equipment I needed would be available?			
Getting on with it			
Did I come to each lesson knowing what I had to do?			
Did I ask for help only when I needed it?			
Did I work well with my friends?			
When things went wrong could I work out what to do about it?			
When things went wrong did I work extra hard to catch up?			

6 Being good at design and technology

Being good at design and technology at the start of key stage 3

You should be able to say:

- what you are going to make;
- who will use your product and what they need and want;
- how you are going to get your ideas;
- whether you are going to work in a group or on your own.

You should be able to show:

- your first design ideas through quick sketching and notes;
- how your designs developed through more drawings with notes and quick modelling with card.

You should be able to:

- follow a schedule to organize your work;
- choose the right hand-tools and simple equipment;
- use these tools and equipment carefully and accurately.

You should be able to:

- show how well your product is made;
- follow a test to show how well your product works;
- write about how well you have worked.

Here is some good work from year 7 students, Ray and Judith. They worked together to design and make glove puppets for a production of 'Noah's Ark' to be shown to a nearby infants' school.

This is good because:

- They knew what they were going to design and make.
- They knew who they were designing for and what they wanted.
- They got books from the library.
- They used an everyday object to help.

This is good because:

- Their work shows where the ideas came from and how they became clearer.

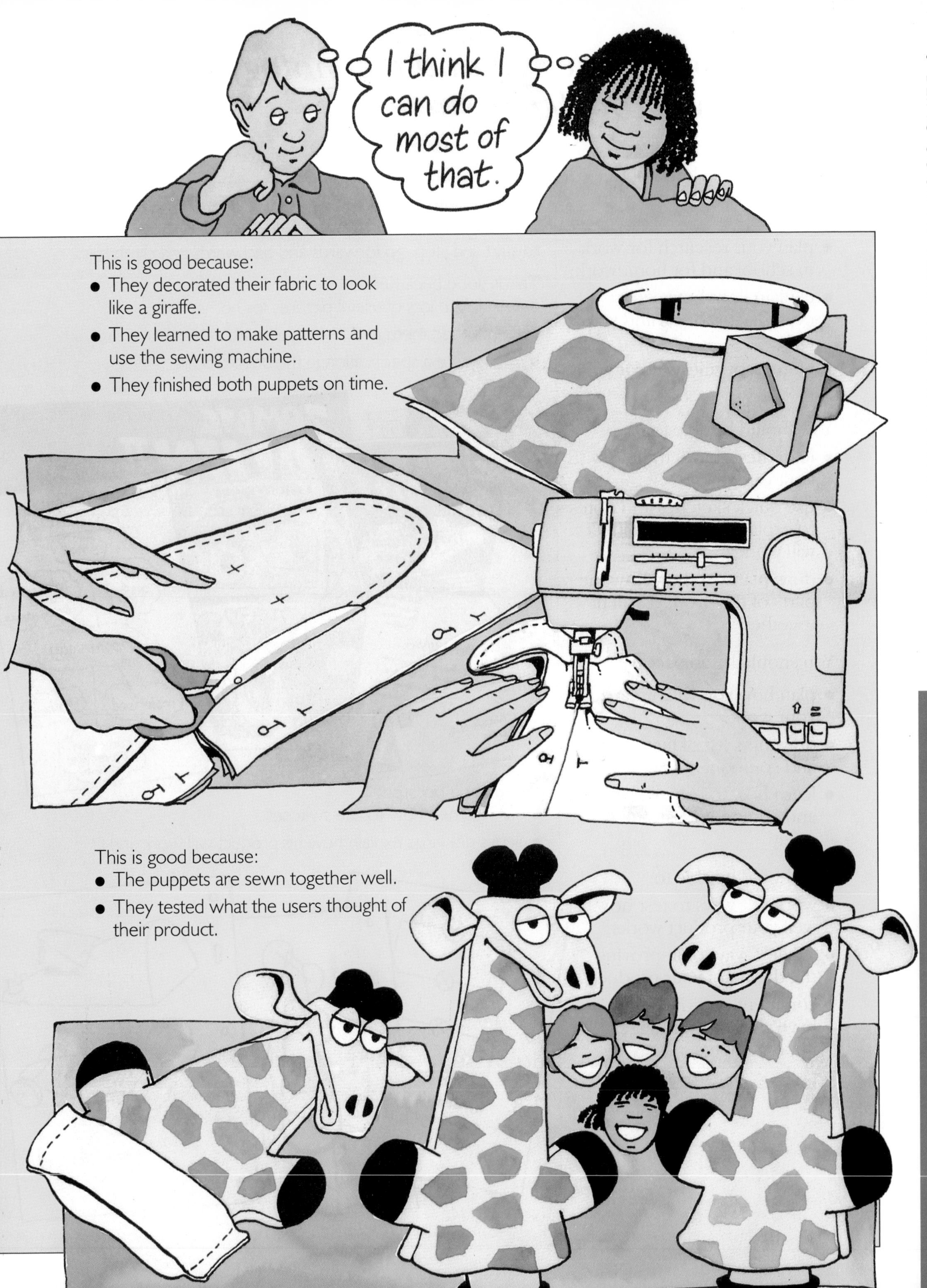
I think I can do most of that.
This is good because:
• They decorated their fabric to look like a giraffe.
• They learned to make patterns and use the sewing machine.
• They finished both puppets on time.
This is good because:
• The puppets are sewn together well.
• They tested what the users thought of their product.

Being good at design and technology half-way through key stage 3

You should be able to:

- use what you know about people to get your design right;
- plan your research for work in school and for homework;
- explain links between everyday products and your task;
- write a specification for your product.

You should be able to:

- learn new things to help with your design;
- use quick sketches and notes to explain how the product will work;
- draw plans to show how the parts of the product will fit together.

You should be able to:

- plan how you will organize your work;
- draw up a list of materials and components needed;
- learn how to use more tools and equipment carefully and safely.

You should be able to:

- work out ways to test how well your product works;
- suggest ways of improving the design of your product;
- comment on how well you have worked and suggest improvements.

Here is some good work from year 8 student, Sam. He was designing and making a space buggy for a model film set. It had to start and stop, go forwards and backwards and climb hills.

This is good because:

- Sam found lots of useful pictures for homework.
- Sam turned them into an image board at school.
- Sam wrote a specification in the bubble chart.

This is good because:

- Sam learned how to use switches.
- Sam's drawings explain how his product will work and fit together.

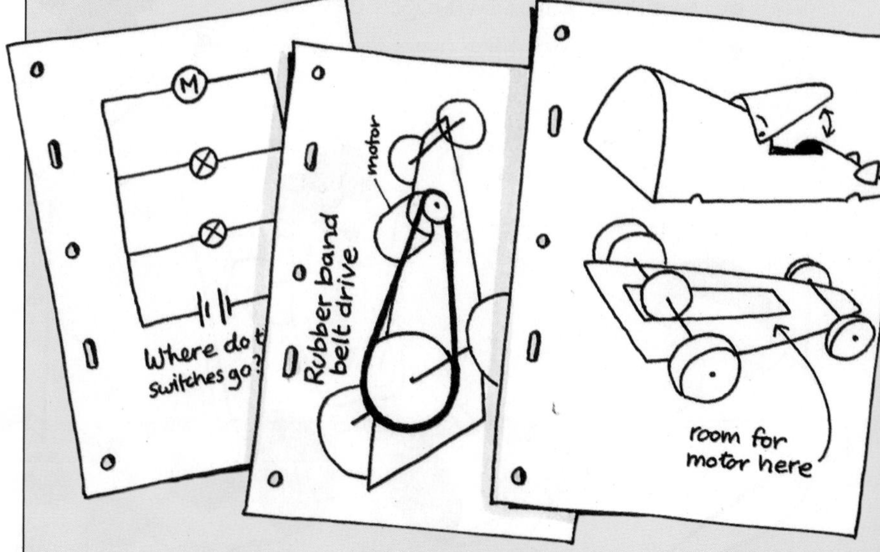

This is good because:

- Sam used a flow chart to plan his work schedule.
- He wrote down what he would need.
- He learned to use a soldering iron properly.

This is good because:

- Sam finished his buggy.
- Sam worked out how to test it and suggested improvements.
- Sam told his teacher that he had got stuck on wiring the reversing switch. This had held him up so he hadn't managed to make a driver figure.

Being good at design and technology at the end of key stage 3

You should be able to:

- build a picture of the consumers and their tastes;
- use research findings to help your design thinking and decision making;
- apply what you know about people to make your design successful;
- explore existing products as a source of design ideas.

You should be able to:

- explore a variety of possible solutions before deciding on one to develop;
- show that the way you have developed your final product makes sense;
- present design proposals so that people will want the product.

You should be able to:

- plan your work and check its progress;
- state clearly the standard of making required;
- make one or more of the final product to that standard.

You should be able to:

- choose ways to test how well the product works and its wider effects;
- suggest ways of improving your product in the light of the tests;
- comment on how well you have worked and identify clear targets for improvement.

Here is some good work from year 9 student, Katie. She had to design some finger-foods with a Mexican theme. This was part of a class project on travel promotion to far-away places.

This is good because:

- Katie has found out what is already on the market and who buys it.
- She has produced an image board of the consumer.
- She has found out about Mexico and Mexican food.
- She has looked at existing similar products and who buys them.

This is good because:

- Katie looked at a range of food wrappings.
- She did preference testing on different fillings.
- She showed how she would present the product.

This is good because:

- Katie has worked out how to make the product.
- She has organized the whole task with a plan.
- She has produced a food product that looks amusing and has the right taste.

This is good because:

- Katie looked at the nutritional content of the food product as well as its novelty appeal.
- Katie found that the pastry in some of the hats was too crumbly and suggested how to put this right.
- She identified the need to make the product easier to use as a clear target for improvement.

7 Getting better at design and technology

Getting better at design and technology at the start of key stage 3

Capability Task snapshot

Measuring accurately

Terry was making shorts for Oxfam. He chose the fabric and used some of his younger brother's shorts as a pattern. When he sewed them up they looked very odd.

Key point
People are three-dimensional: you always have to allow for their roundness.

What went wrong?
Pieces of shorts don't look like the finished garment. Terry should have used a pattern. It is never worth rushing things.

So put it right like this

Joining carefully

Tracey designed a hexagonal gift box covered in ladybirds to be sold in a garden centre gift shop. She made the card net really well and her ladybirds looked as if they had just landed on it. But when she came to put her box together it just wouldn't work. What had she done wrong?

Key point
The bits you can't see from the outside are just as important as the bits you can see when you are making a structure.

What went wrong?
The design only becomes a box when you can stick the sides together. Tracey should have included gluing flaps.

So put it right like this

Capability Task snapshot

Finishing touches

Salim followed the recipe for fairy cakes. He decided to decorate them with icing. He measured the ingredients, and mixed them together but the icing ran off the cakes into pools. They tasted good but looked messy.

Key point
Follow recipe instructions exactly to get the best results.

What went wrong?
Sometimes it's not enough knowing what to do. You have to know how to do it and use your judgement. You have to take an active part in designing and making decisions.

So put it right like this

Capability Task snapshot

Getting better at design and technology half-way through key stage 3

Understanding materials

Leroy made strawberry jam for the summer fair. It was delicious. His aunt bought some but less than a week later it had gone mouldy. Leroy had been very careful to sterilize the pots, so where had the mould come from?

Capability Task snapshot

Key point
Study recipes carefully. Don't change them without finding out what might happen.

What went wrong?
Leroy should have read the labels from low-sugar jam to see if gelatine was there or if there were special storage instructions. He should have asked his teacher's advice.

So put it right like this

Working with a specification

Frances made a prototype school games bag that matched the uniform and was even waterproof. She added extra pockets for shampoo and brushes and a safe compartment for money. When the class designs were shown to the parents, Frances' design was rejected although everyone thought her ideas were good. How come?

Key point
Keep checking against the specification as you are working on your product.

What went wrong?
Frances didn't really consider any other user than herself. She didn't try to meet the specification. All her energy went into her bright ideas instead of the task set.

So put it right like this

Capability Task snapshot

Communicating clearly

Ruth couldn't wait to make her 'Jill-in-the-box'. She made a good working model – Jill popped up every time! She spent ages making sure that the spring mechanism worked. Her teacher commented that there was not much written work.

Key point
Drawing and writing help you and your teacher with your project.

What went wrong?
Ruth rushed into making a working model and didn't think through how her toy would look. The teacher couldn't help because Ruth had not drawn what it would look like.

So put it right like this

Capability Task snapshot

Getting better at design and technology at the end of key stage 3

Targets and deadlines

Sarjit's design proposal for a bath overfill alarm showed exactly how the circuit and casing would be made. She worked hard at making the printed circuit board and at soldering all the components in place. It was a pity that in the end she used a painted cigarette packet for the case!

Capability Task snapshot

Key point
You must work out what needs to be done *and* fit it into a time plan before you start making.

What went wrong?
Sarjit did not leave herself enough time to produce the case. She got too involved with getting the circuit board perfect. She should have worked out a time plan which covered the circuit and the case.

So put it right like this

Using technical understanding

Darren was the cartoon whiz-kid of the class. He decided that his moving-face toy would have ears that waggled, eyes that blinked, teeth that chattered and a nose that dripped. In the end he made one with a hat that rocked when you pulled a string. How come?

Key point
You have to balance your ideas with what you know.

What went wrong?
Darren was too ambitious. He should have spent more time finding out about mechanisms he could use for his funny face.

So put it right like this

Capability Task snapshot

Checking details

Ben spent ages producing an air-brushed poster to encourage nursery children to recycle plastics and tins. His slogan was 'Kick the cans in the van' and he used images of football boots and football scarves. Ben couldn't understand why no one in the nursery understood the message.

Key point
To design something useful you have to test the market.

What went wrong?
Ben did not research the users. He put his energy into producing a nicely finished product that did not do the job. He should have listened to his teacher's advice.

So put it right like this

Capability Task snapshot

8 Using other subjects in design and technology

Using mathematics

Does your heart sink when people mention maths? Do you find it difficult sometimes? Or even boring? Or do you enjoy doing sums and solving problems?

Either way, you will find that you have been using maths in design and technology without even realizing it.

Have you ever:

- weighed out ingredients?

- measured materials?

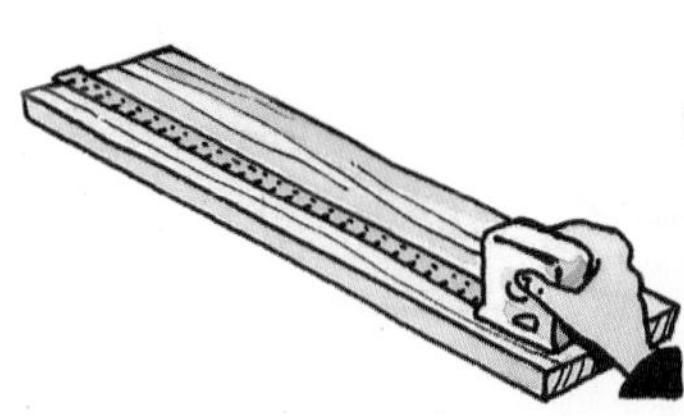

- drawn shapes and patterns?

- used a mechanism?

- cut materials to the right size?

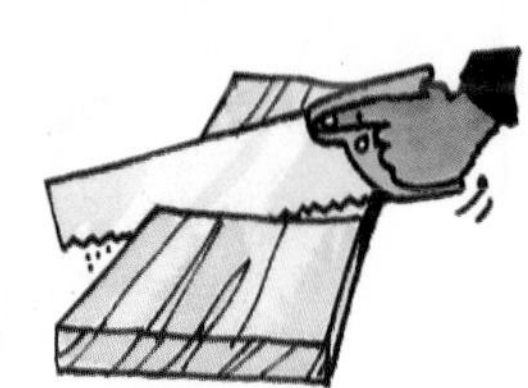

Then you have been using maths!

What's in it for you?

If you use maths, your designing and making will improve because it will be more accurate, work properly and look better, as these examples show.

Where did Ahmed use maths?

Ahmed designed and made a healthy single-dish meal to introduce spicy food as part of a Mexican food range.

Can you spot where Ahmed has used maths?

Using mathematics can help you to:

- evaluate consumer likes and dislikes;
- convert ounces to grams;
- measure materials;
- estimate amounts.

Where did Jane use maths?

Jane designed and made a pull-along circus toy with a mechanism that is powered by the axles.

Can you spot where Jane has used maths?

Using mathematics can help you to:

- design parts precisely;
- draw shapes accurately;
- put moving parts in the right places so that they work.

Where did Kim use maths?

Kim designed and made a bag based on a rectangle with an appliqué motif.

Can you spot where Kim has used maths?

Using mathematics can help you to:

- design 3D shapes with nets;
- mark out straight and curved lines;
- work out how much material you need;
- design motifs using geometric shapes and symmetry.

Using science

Do you ever think that the science you do in school does not have much to do with the real world? Do the experiments seem a bit pointless? Is it sometimes difficult to make sense of the ideas? Or do you really enjoy it and find the ideas interesting?
  Either way, you will find that you have been using science in design and technology without even realizing it.

Have you ever:

- tested the properties of fabrics?
- drawn a circuit diagram?
- made and tested a model bridge?
- cleaned metals with acid?
- changed the ingredients in a recipe?

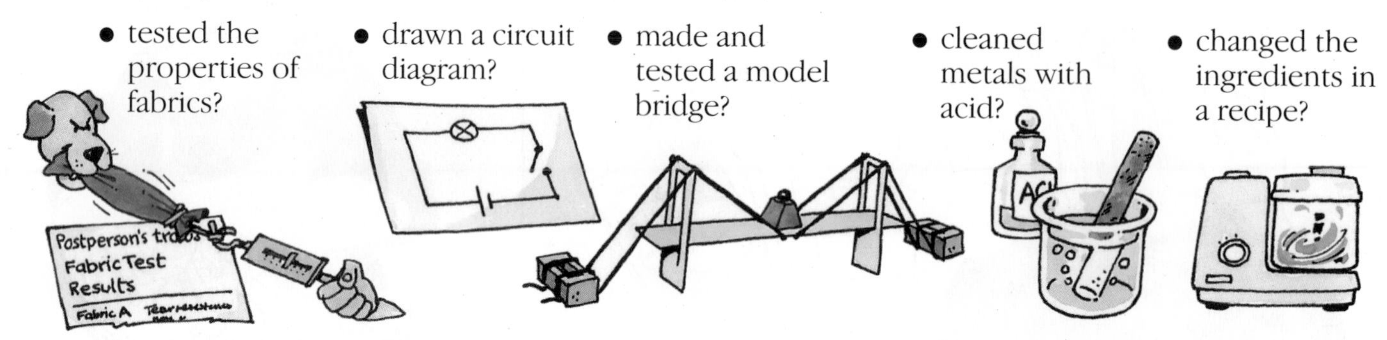

Then you have been using science!

What's in it for you?

If you use science your designing and making will improve because you will know more about the properties of materials, understand better how things work and be able to design better tests for your products, as these examples show.

Where did Sarah use science?

Sarah designed and made a high-energy snack food bar suitable for cyclists.

Can you spot where Sarah has used science?

Using science can help you to:

- understand about energy;
- use energy information;
- measure the energy people use when doing things;
- design food products for sporting activities.

Where did Louise use science?

Louise designed and made a circuit to light a model house.

Can you spot where Louise has used science?

Using science can help you to:

- design circuits;
- draw circuit diagrams;
- choose the right electrical components;
- de-bug circuits that don't work.

Where did Carl use science?

Carl designed and made a display system for selling books.

Can you spot where Carl has used science?

Using science can help you to:

- understand forces;
- design structures that are strong;
- design structures that are stiff;
- design structures that don't fall over.

Using art

Do you find art lessons difficult? Do the pencil and the paintbrush seem to have minds of their own? Do you find it hard to think up things to draw? Or do you really enjoy it and like mixing colours and making pictures?

Either way, you will find that you have been using art in design and technology without even realizing it.

Have you ever:

- drawn real life people or things?
- mixed colours?
- sketched ideas?
- chosen lettering shapes?
- looked at other people's art or designs to give you ideas?
- styled a product you are going to make?

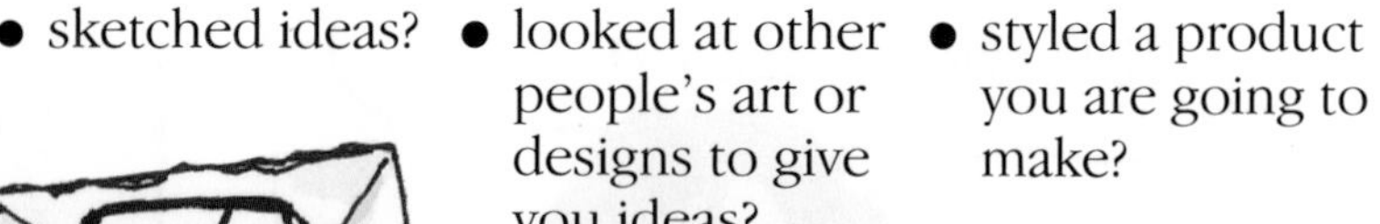

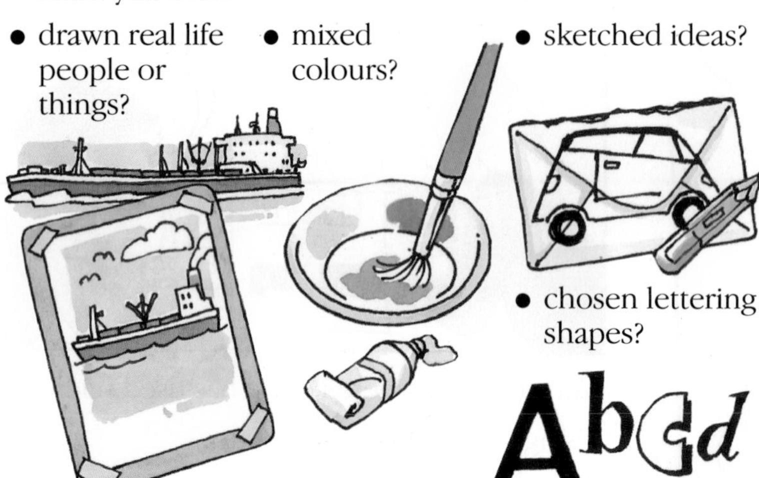

Then you have been using art!

What's in it for you?

If you use art, your designing and making will improve because your sketches of designs and your presentation drawings will be better and your products will be much more attractive to look at.

Where did Kevin use art?

Kevin designed and made a gift box for selling in a zoo.

Can you spot where Kevin has used art?

Using art can help you to:

- look at animals and objects to see what they are like;
- look at pictures of animals and objects to see what they are like;
- draw complicated things simply;
- choose the right colours.

Where did M'kana use art?

M'Kana designed and made a kaftan with batik decoration for Third World Week.

I don't see how they manage to get it so neat. I keep on splodging it. I think I need to make my pattern really simple.

I want the patterns to be in the colours of Africa - hot and dusty. I'm not sure which ones to choose.

Can you spot where M'kana has used art?

Using art can help you to:

- explore images and styles from other cultures;
- use techniques from other places in the world;
- mix colours to reflect places or moods;
- design patterns.

Where did Marisa use art?

Marisa designed and made a set of sports medals for the school netball team.

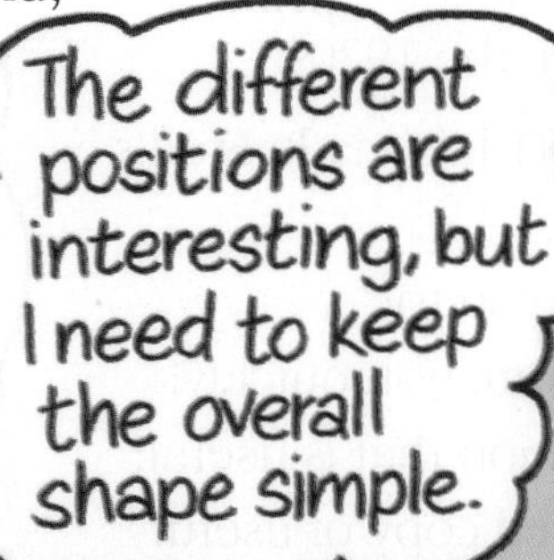

Can you spot where Marisa has used art?

Using art can help you to:

- look at figures in action;
- capture movement with still images;
- model with card;
- mix colours that look like materials.

Using information technology

Do you find it hard to see where information technology (IT) fits into designing and making things?

IT is used in all subjects, including design and technology. It opens up new and faster ways of doing things.

Whenever you use a computer you are using IT.

What's in it for you?

If you use IT your designing and making will improve. You will be able to:

- research other people's designs more quickly;
- handle and present your own information more easily;
- make parts for your products more accurately and quickly;
- control some of your products with a computer.

Where did Fred use IT?

Fred designed and made a printed T-shirt to celebrate the 1920s.

Can you see how IT has made Fred's life easier?

Using IT can help you to:

- scan lots of information quickly;
- choose information that is useful;
- produce a printed copy of useful information.

Where did Nicola use IT?

Nicola designed and made some simple jewellery for the school fete.

Can you see how IT has made Nicola's life easier?

Using IT can help you to:

- make things faster;
- make things more accurately;
- make things that would otherwise be too difficult.

Where did Salina use IT?

Salina designed and made biscuits for the school fete.

Can you see how IT has made Salina's life easier?

Using IT can help you to:

- explore what happens when you change things;
- make decisions about prices.

Where did Darren use IT?

Darren designed and made a robot arm to attract attention at the school fete.

Can you see how IT has made Darren's life easier?

Using IT can help you to:

- control machines that you have made.

9 Being safe in designing and making

Introducing some important words

A **hazard** is anything which might cause harm or damage. A kitchen knife is a hazard. It is very sharp and there is a chance that you could cut yourself with it. This chance is called the **risk**. You can work out how big the risk is by thinking about whether the harm or damage is likely to happen. This is called **assessing** the risk. This is not always easy.

If a chef uses a sharp knife then the risk of an accident is low. If a small child uses the knife then the risk is high.

Risk control is the action taken to ensure that the harm or damage is less likely to happen. The chef has been trained to use the knife and he is always careful. This training and his way of working control the risk. The child is prevented from using the knife and this controls the risk.

Both the chef and the child are in safe situations because the risk has been controlled, so the chance of harm or damage is small.

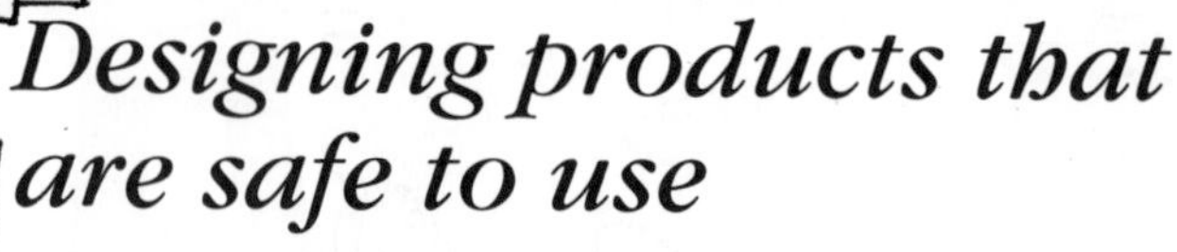

Designing products that are safe to use

When you design a product, think about the hazards there might be in the way it is used. Your design should try to control any risk by making the risk as small as possible. Here are some products being used with questions to help you assess the hazards.

1 Who is likely to get hurt here?

2 Can designers help people to use their products carefully?

3 What are the risks here?
4 What can be done to prevent them?

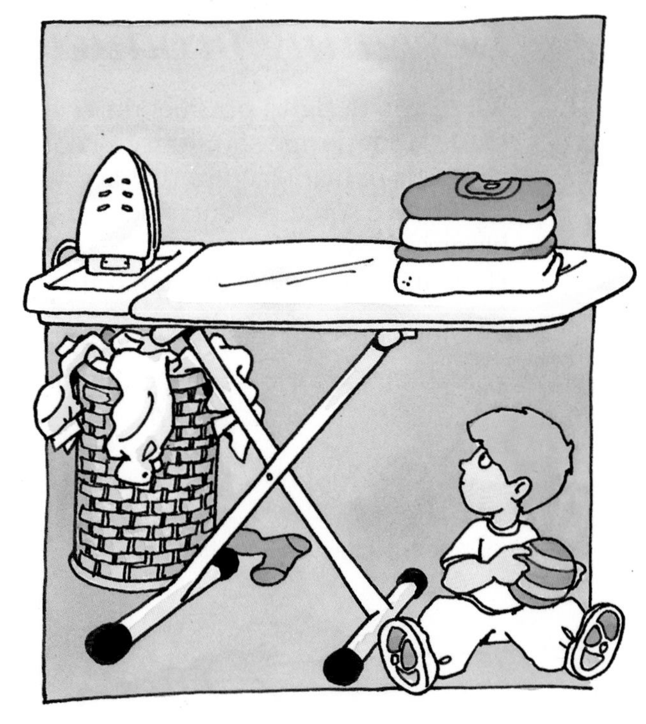

7 How can you tell that the iron is on and hot?
8 What are the risks in this situation?

5 What are the risks from using these wrappers?
6 Who is most likely to be in danger?

9 What are the risks here?
10 Would you want to make roller skating completely safe?

Designing products that are safe to make

When you design a product think about the hazards there might be in the way it is made. Your design should try to control these risks by choosing materials and methods of manufacture that are as safe as possible.

Here are some products being made with questions to help you assess the hazards.

How many of the following hazards can you spot?

- being cut
- becoming deaf
- getting strained
- getting blinded
- being burned
- being poisoned
- getting bruised

1 What are the risks here?
2 How would you control them?

5 What are the risks here?
6 How would you control them?

3 What are the risks here?
4 How would you control them?

7 What are the risks here?
8 How would you control them?

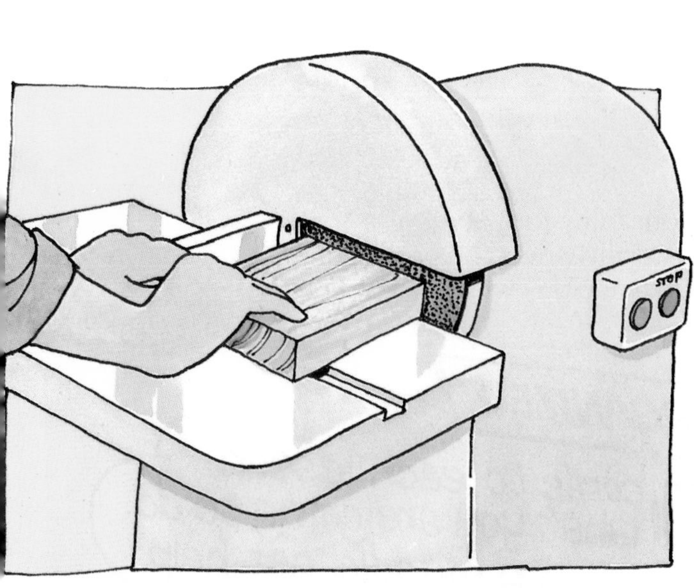

Effects over time

Some hazards are not very dangerous in small amounts but with regular exposure over a period of time they cause serious damage to health. For example, it is important to wear a mask to prevent breathing in fibres and dust. It is important that any liquid or process that gives off fumes is used in a well-ventilated area or fume cupboard.

9 What are the risks here?
10 How would you control them?

Sources of information

Where should you look for information to help you with risk assessment? A useful place to start is with your teachers. They are responsible for showing you safe ways to use tools and equipment, so they can give you guidance. Instructions that come with a product are important. To use a product safely you should follow the instructions carefully. This applies particularly to food, cosmetics and medicines.

Safety standards are the government-agreed regulations for the design of a wide range of products. Consumer magazines often contain articles about the product safety. Ask your teacher to help you use these published materials.

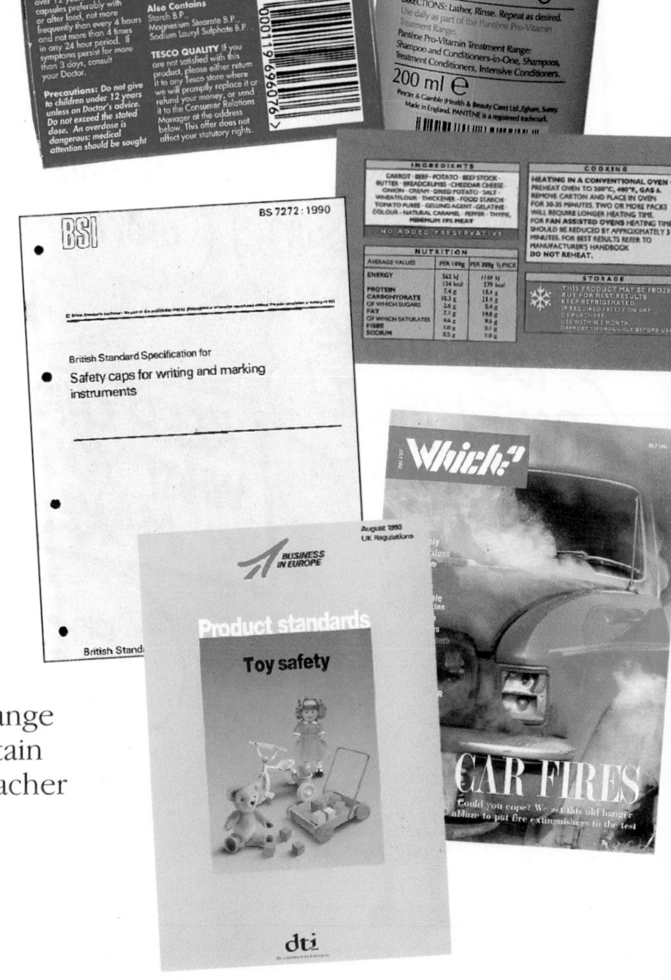

10 Styles of learning

Working on your own

In design and technology you have to take responsibility for your work. You often work on your own over several weeks, especially when you are making the thing you have designed. It is important to manage this well. Here are some rules for working on your own:

DON'T PANIC

Find out what makes you panic in D&T. Get help as soon as you start to worry. Try to stay CALM.

GET ORGANIZED

Try to come to each lesson knowing what you are going to do. If you get in a muddle get help before it's TOO LATE.

PLAN CAREFULLY

Your plan should tell you what you have to do AND when you have to do it by. If you get behind work out ways to CATCH UP.

THINK ABOUT YOUR STRENGTHS AND WEAKNESSES

You know what you're GOOD at – use this well. You know what you're BAD at – work out ways to get BETTER.

KEEP ALL YOUR WORK SAFELY

Lost work slows you down. Lost work loses marks. DON'T LOSE IT!

KEEP CHECKING THAT WHAT YOU ARE DOING MAKES SENSE

Don't get so wrapped up in one part of the task that you can't do the other parts properly. Use the specification to make sure that what you're doing is SENSIBLE.

Working with others

Getting help from your teacher

Your teacher's job is to teach you to be good at design and technology. Sometimes your teacher will help you do things that you are finding difficult. At other times your teacher will make you do things for yourself. This balance of helping and standing back is important if you are to become capable. Your teachers are always there to teach you and you can get the best from them by following these rules:

Don't ask for help when the teacher is very busy organizing the class, as at the beginning or end of a lesson.

When you ask a question make sure it isn't something you could have worked out easily for yourself.

If you need materials ask for them well in advance and use a written reminder note.

If you are not sure what to do next, think about what you *could* do before you ask.

If you are not sure how to do something, think about how you *might* do it before you ask for help.

Remember- your teachers are keen to have short conversations that help you to make decisions. They can't spend a lot of time telling you things.

Getting help from your friends

Often it is easier to have ideas or work things out if you talk to other people. This isn't cheating; it is the way people work in the world outside school. You won't do your friends' work for them and they won't do yours, but by working together you will all do better. Here are some rules for working with your friends:

Clear communication always helps in designing and making. ▶

Don't gossip; make sure you talk about design and technology.

Talk and listen carefully.

Treat other people's ideas with respect.

If you are tackling a team project decide who is doing what and by when.

If you say you will do something then do it - don't forget.

11 Looking after your work

Recording your ideas

What should I record?

It is important to tell the story of your designing and making for two reasons:

- telling the story as you work will help you to get better;
- your teacher can see how you are doing and show you how to make progress.

These are the sorts of things you should record for a Capability Task.

Capability Tasks
I need to record:
- The specification for the product.
- Where my ideas came from.
- How my ideas developed.
- What I am going to make.
- How I'm going to make it.
- Any changes I make along the way, and why I made them.
- How well the product works.
- What effects the product will have.

How should I record things?

You have to choose the best way of recording your work, but all of the following will be useful.

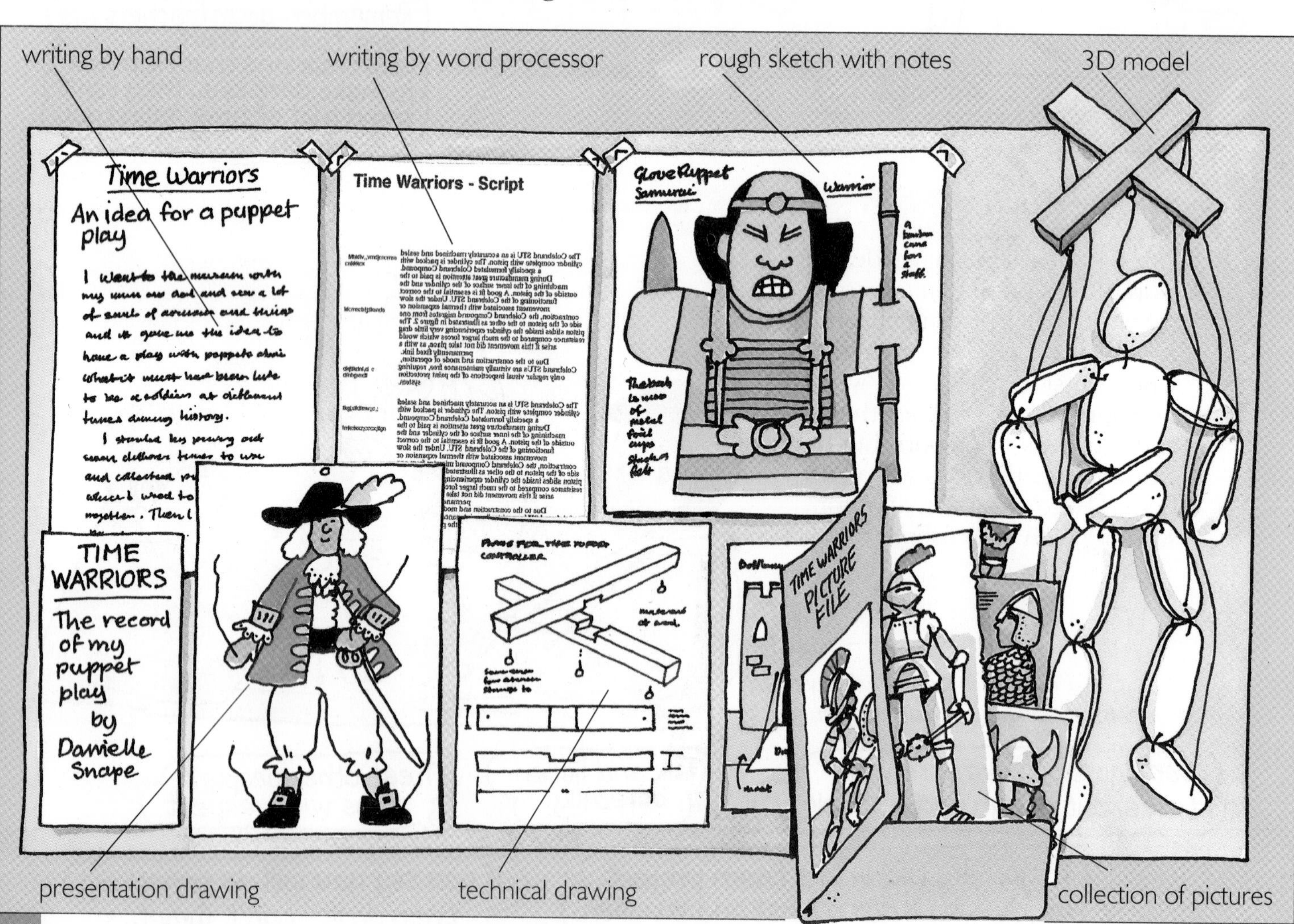

Building up a portfolio

It is important to keep your work safe during a designing and making task. This is so that at the end of the task you have a record of what you did and why you did it.

A travelling folder

You will need this for everyday work. It will contain just what you need for a lesson. It should fit into your school bag so that it is easy to carry.

Don't keep everything in it, because:

- it will get too heavy to carry;
- if you do lose it you won't have lost everything.

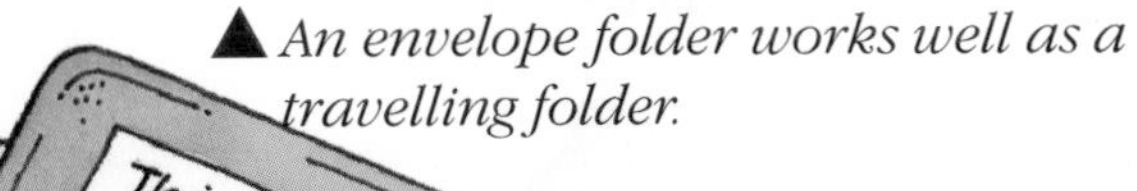

▲ *An envelope folder works well as a travelling folder.*

A project folder

You will need a folder to keep the complete story of your designing and making. You will probably keep this at home most of the time but your teacher will want to see it regularly. It is important that:

- you keep it in a safe place;
- it can hold the record of a complete project in the right order.

▲ *A ring-binder makes a good project folder.*

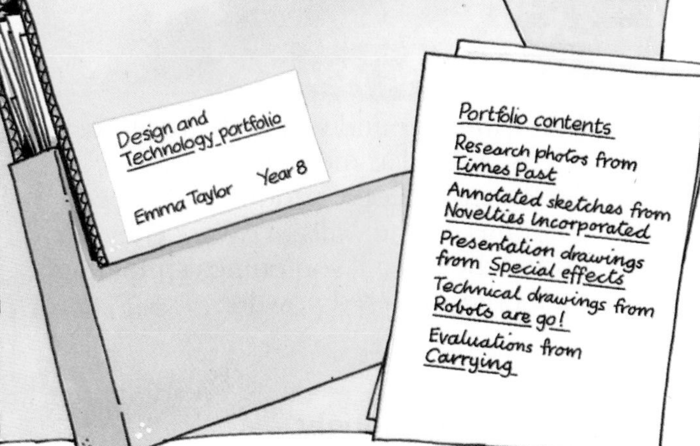

▲ *A stiff case like this makes a good portfolio.*

A portfolio for the best examples

A portfolio is a collection of pieces from different designing and making tasks which shows the very best of your work. Your teacher will help you decide what to keep in your portfolio. It is important that you:

- label each piece of work clearly with your name, the task it is from and the date;
- keep a list of the work in your portfolio and make sure it is up-to-date.

1 The first design technologists

Our early ancestors used design and technology skills to meet their needs, just as we do today

People have lived on the Earth for over a million years. Although early people did not write things down, we know a lot about how they lived. They used stone tools, so they must have worked with hard materials. They used fires for cooking and changed materials by heating them. By about 50 000 years ago, people were very much like us. They had the same **needs** as us and used **design and technology skills** to meet them.

▲ *Our ancestors cooked on open fires.*

▲ *An early burial.*

1 Think about the people in your community. What basic needs do they all share? Think of the *need*, not the things that meet the need. For example, people need food – a hamburger is just one way of meeting this need.

2 List these needs. Then, write down the different ways people meet each need.

People like you

Food, **shelter** and **warmth** are all basic needs. As well as meeting these basic needs, early people produced detailed paintings on the walls of caves. They also buried their dead, sometimes sprinkling the bodies with red powder.

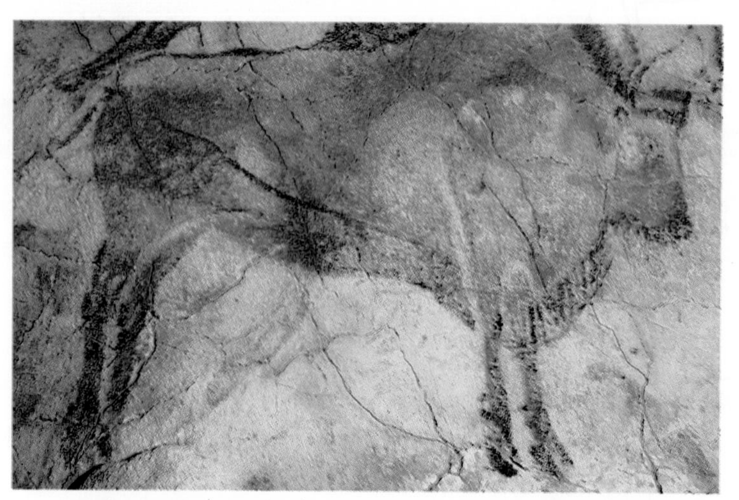

▲ *This cave painting met early people's need to express themselves through art.*

Pause for thought

What needs did these early people meet? Were they meeting needs to build up communities, for friendship and to express themselves?

Early people used their skills as design technologists to meet their needs.

3 Are there any more needs you would like to add to your list?

4 Make a list of different ways in which we use energy to meet our needs.

Meeting needs using energy

We take for granted energy from many different sources, not thinking how much we depend upon it. Every day we all use hundreds of energy 'slaves', like the battery in a digital watch or camcorder. Each person in a rich country has power working for them, day and night, at a rate of 12 kilowatts. A strong person can only work at a rate of about a third of one kilowatt!

Early people met many of their needs, for example the need to hunt for food, by using the energy from their bodies. Sometimes they used tools to help them, for example a sling – a leather cup with two cords. You put a pebble into the cup and whirl it in a circle around your head. After three or four turns it is moving much faster than your arm can. When you let go of one of the cords, the pebble flies a great distance – as much as two hundred metres. (Please don't try this yourself. It could be very dangerous.)

Cave paintings show early people hunting with bows and arrows. A bow stores energy when you pull the string slowly back. When you let go of the string, the rapid release of energy makes the arrow fly hundreds of metres.

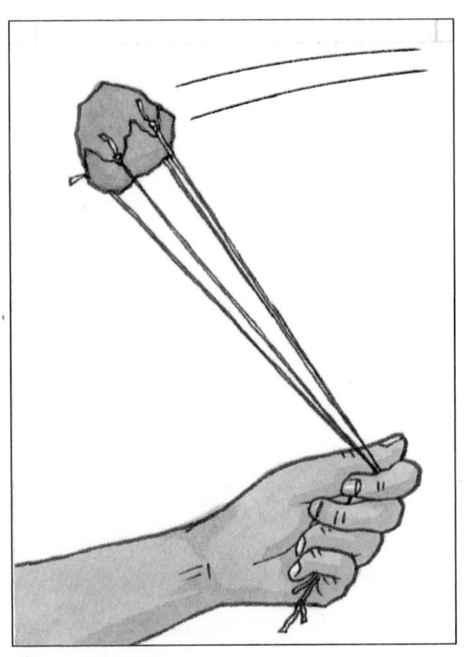

▲ *Slings enabled hunters to throw pebbles much further.*

▲ *Hunting as a group increases the chances of success.*

Using tools

People meet many of their needs by making things. Often they use tools. Some tools – for example, an iron – are specially designed to do a particular job. Others can be used for a variety of jobs.

▲ *The marks on this flint axe head show how it was made.*

1 Produce a list of the tools and equipment in your home.

2 Which tools are general purpose?

3 Which are used for one specific job?

Many tools are based on a sharp cutting edge, for example a food processor, scissors, a wood plane or a pencil sharpener. Before people learnt how to extract metals, they made their tools out of natural materials such as stone, bone and wood. The first stone tools were no more than pebbles with a cutting edge. Very gradually, tool-making skills improved until, in the late Stone Age, people were making beautiful, highly polished stone tools. These included flint axe heads, knives, arrow heads and sharp-pointed tools for stitching.

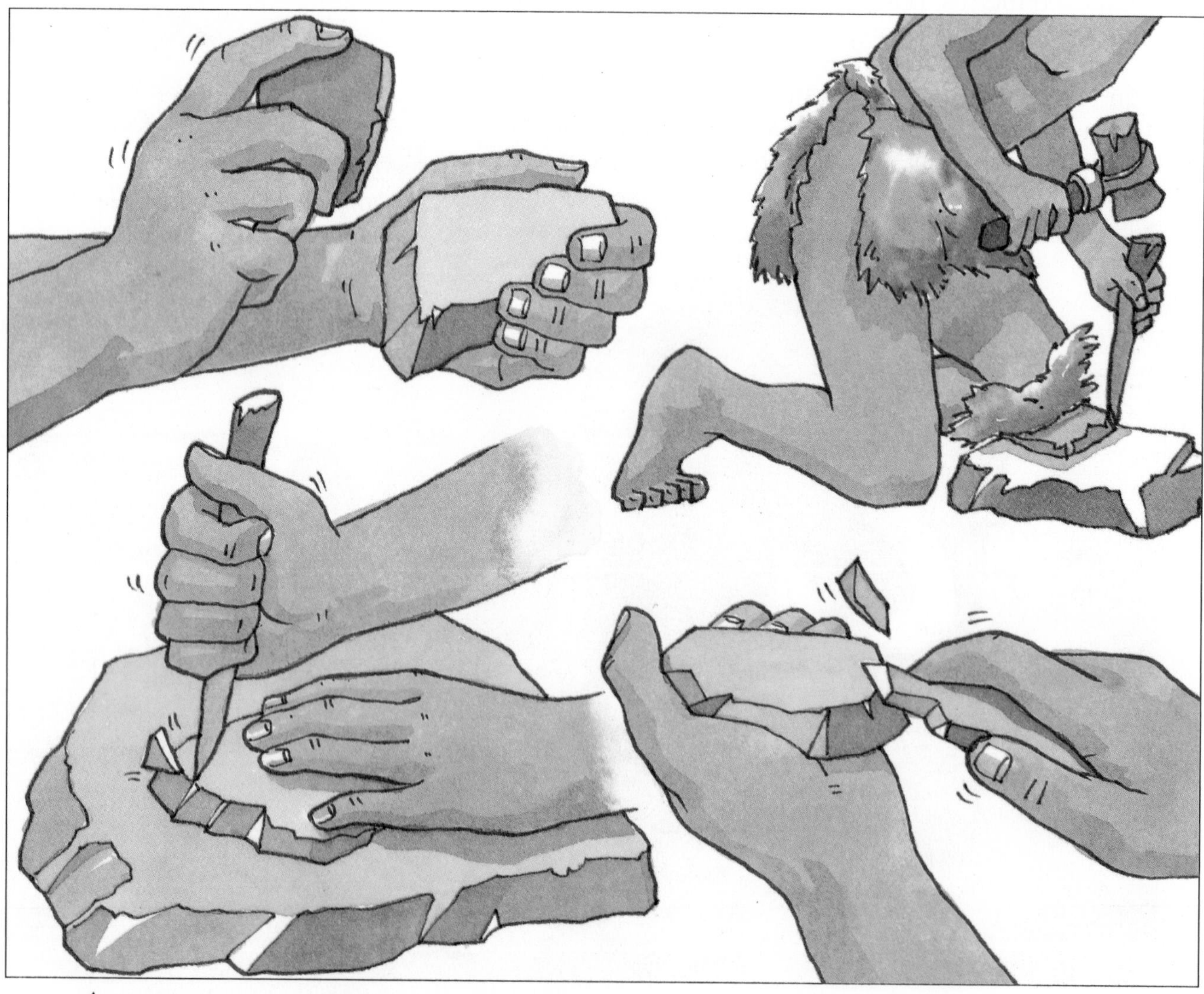

▲ *People living in different places used different technologies for making flint axe heads.*

Flint is a very hard type of stone which can be chipped to give an extremely sharp cutting edge. You can even cut tissue paper with it. It is difficult to make a piece of flint into a useful tool. You have to hit it in just the right place for a flake to fly off. Expert flint workers can make the cutting edge they need by pressing at the right place with a pointed stick or piece of horn.

Pause for thought
How might early people have made curved blades from flint?

But some tools are almost impossible to make from a single lump of flint, for example sickles with long curved blades, and saws with pointed teeth.

Early people made these complicated tools out of a lot of tiny flint blades called **microliths**. First, they made a wooden holder in the shape of the saw or sickle blade and carved a deep groove in it. Then microliths were fixed into the groove with pitch or resin.

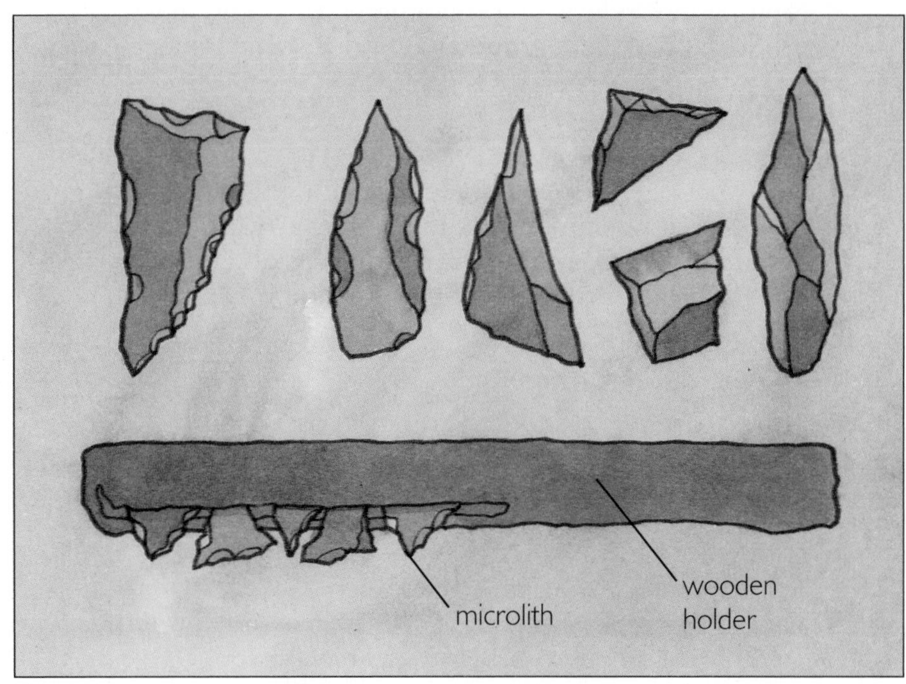

▲ *Several small flint microliths were used to make the compound blade.*

Stones for cooking

There is a lot of evidence that early people used fire for cooking. Large stones separated the flames from the food. Why did people need to do this? As the stones got hot they could be used to cook small pieces of meat or to bake simple oat cakes. Smaller stones were used to bring liquids to the boil by plunging the red hot stones into pots of liquid. In this way food could be stewed in pots that could not be heated directly.

4 Early people used their skills as design technologists to meet their needs. People today have the same needs and meet them in a variety of ways. Go back to your first list of human needs. Do you think that people today are meeting these needs in the best possible way?

5 Can we learn anything from our earliest ancestors?

6 How do you think they lifted the stones into the liquid?

▲ *Cooking stones from early people found in France.*

2 Designing out crime

Design and technology resources can help prevent crime

Newspapers, television programmes and radio news reports all highlight crime as a serious social issue.

Is it a problem?

Older people often give the impression that crime is new, that 'it wasn't like that in my day'. Government crime figures released each year make frightening reading. There are different types of crime:

- crimes against people;
- crimes against property.

Things that are considered crimes in one country may not be in another. Some things are now illegal which in the past were not.

1 Look through one day's newspapers. Cut out all the stories about crimes and put them in order from most serious to least serious. How did you decide the order? Write down some of the reasons for your decisions.

2 List the things that make one crime more serious than another. Do your friends agree with you? Why might house owners, the police or old people disagree with you?

New technologies – new crimes

As technology changes so do the possibilities for crime. Computer databases allow companies to be more efficient but they also provide opportunities for computer fraud. Car stereo systems can make a long journey more interesting, but a car with a cassette or CD player or radio is more likely to be broken into.

3 Think about some of the technological changes which have taken place over the last twenty years. Write down how one of these changes could lead to new possibilities for crime.

Pause for thought

Do newspaper and television reports make the crime problem seem more serious than it really is?

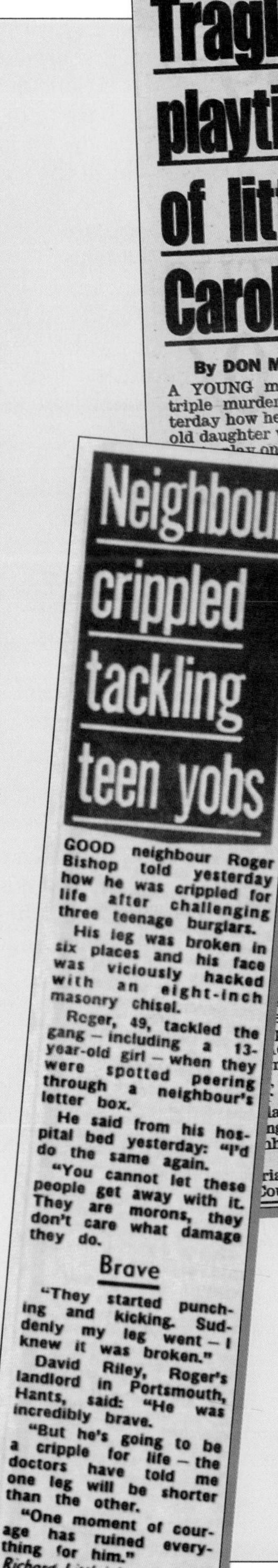

Tragic playtime of little Caroline

By DON MACKAY

A YOUNG mum told a triple murder trial yesterday how her five-year-old daughter was allowed

Neighbour crippled tackling teen yobs

GOOD neighbour Roger Bishop told yesterday how he was crippled for life after challenging three teenage burglars.

His leg was broken in six places and his face was viciously hacked with an eight-inch masonry chisel.

Roger, 49, tackled the gang – including a 13-year-old girl – when they were spotted peering through a neighbour's letter box.

He said from his hospital bed yesterday: "I'd do the same again.

"You cannot let these people get away with it. They are morons, they don't care what damage they do.

Brave

"They started punching and kicking. Suddenly my leg went – I knew it was broken."

David Riley, Roger's landlord in Portsmouth, Hants, said: "He was incredibly brave.

"But he's going to be a cripple for life – the doctors have told me one leg will be shorter than the other.

"One moment of courage has ruined everything for him."

Richard Littlejohn – Page 9

PALS MADE PERFECT £20 NOTES ON A PHOTOCOPIER

£1.5m duds 'best cops had ever seen'

Gun death trial told of gentle victim

THE flatmate of a Cambridge graduate believed to have been killed in a case of mistaken identity told the Old Bailey yesterday: "I don't think he had ever done anything wrong in his life."

Martin Jacks, 23, a trainee accountant, was shot at close range by three masked men who burst into his flat in Putney, southwest London

and Roland Thorp, 26, both of Chessington, southwest London, deny murdering Mr Jacks last June.

Simon Bourne, 24, who was at Cambridge with Mr Jacks and shared the flat with him, told the court his friend did not have a care in the world. Mr Bourne, a management consultant, said that on the day of the shooting he had ... sitting on the ... cricket.

... jury: "He was ... normal self. He ... relaxing and ... studying." Mr Bourne said that when he returned from shopping there were police officers at the flat who told him that his friend had been murdered.

Mr Bourne said: "I don't think Martin had ever done anything wrong in his entire life. He was a gentle, easy-going, laid-back person."

Nigel Sweeney, for the prosecution, said the victim was a wholly innocent young man. "I am sure no one is going to say a word against him during this trial."

The trial continues.

DEALER ACCUSED OF £250m FAKE DEALS

OP Wall Street broker Joseph Jett is said to hav... onned his bosses out of £6million in commission b... laiming to have made deals worth £250million.

Jett, 36, has just been sacked from his job as chief bon... rader at giant American investment bank Kidder Peabo... after an investigation discovered that massive deals h... been faked.

Kidder's British-born boss Michael Carpenter had been so impres... by Jett's work that he presented him with the company's high... honour—the chairman's award for excellence—at ... number is

boy, 5, with tractor tyre

YOUNGSTER Glen Chappell was crushed by a tractor tyre rolled by thugs as a joke.

And as the five year old was smashed against a lamppost by the 5ft tyre they ran away laughing.

Frightened Glen needed eight stitches to one eye and may be scarred for life. Yesterday police said the tyre could easily have killed him.

The boy was attacked while out buying his mother a birthday present from local shops

... cola, 22, and ... albrookdale, ... nd them and ... ul out of the ... a Fiat Uno being driven up the hill.

The 18-year-old driver

EXPRESS REPORTER

...ngela, from Telford, ...ropshire, said: "This was deliberate, and my child is suffering through someone's joke.

ily have been fatal. He could have been killed by the tyre itself — it was so big — or knocked into the path of a passing car.

"We could easily have been looking at a man-

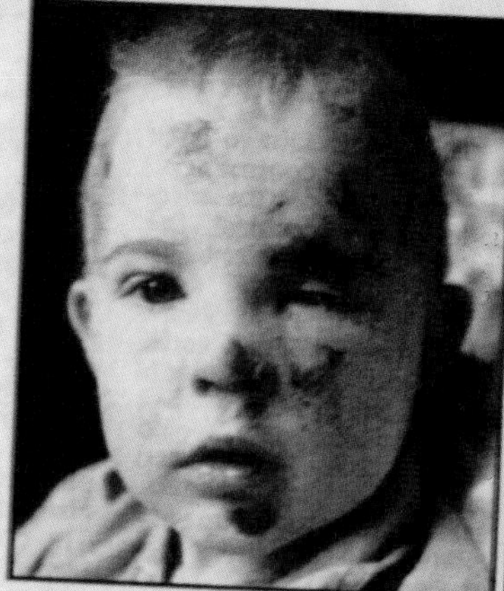

GLEN: May be scarred for life

Blind man attacked as he exercises dog

A BLIND man exercising his guide dog had his nose broken in a cowardly attack by a fellow pet owner.

Philip Smith, 37, had just let his cross retriever off the leash in playing fields when he heard a shout "Keep your dog away from mine." Then he was punched in the face and sent reeling by a number of blows. He suffered cuts to the face which needed several stitches.

"All I could do was put my hands up to try and protect my face," said Philip, of North Shields, Tyne and Wear. A man was yesterday helping police inquiries.

A variety of solutions

Any problem can be solved in a variety of ways. Think about car crime – cars being stolen or broken into. Possible ways of tackling this type of crime include:

- car alarms;
- improved street lighting;
- persuading people not to leave valuables on view in their cars;
- supervised car parks;
- steering-wheel locks;
- more police officers walking the beat;
- improving public transport;
- combination locks;
- neighbourhood watch schemes;
- persuading people not to commit the crime;
- persuading people not to use their cars at night;
- giving everyone a free car so that they no longer need to steal one.

Each suggestion has good and bad points. Car alarms can deter criminals but they are a nuisance if they are set off accidentally. Car ignitions can be fitted with combination locks but the owner might forget the combination. Some of the suggestions seem ridiculous: it would be far too expensive to give everyone a free car. However, some countries provide people with free bicycles in the cities. Some of the ideas on the list are to do with changing the way people think and behave.

To meet some of the suggestions a design technologist might need to design:

- a **product** such as a lock or an alarm;
- a **place** such as a car park or well-lit street; or
- a **system** which might involve people and things, such as neighbourhood watch schemes which rely on people, visible stickers and telephones.

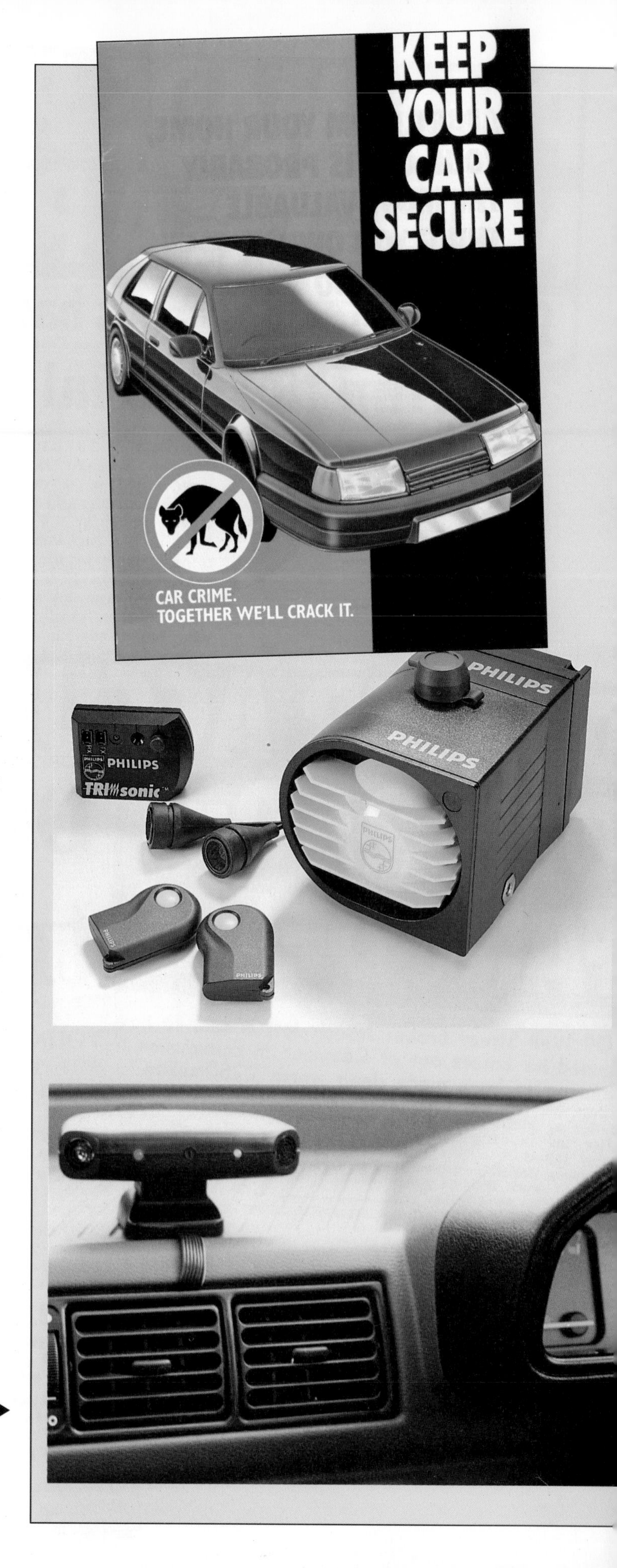

Products and systems to prevent car crime. ▶

1 Bicycles are often stolen. List possible reasons for this and the places where it is most likely to happen.

2 Write down suggestions for products, places or systems which could be designed to reduce bicycle theft.

A matter of priorities

If we had unlimited resources we might be able to prevent most crime. However, resources are limited. We have to make choices. For instance, in order to reduce crime on a housing estate, money could be used to:

- employ a security guard;
- improve the general environment;
- build a youth club;
- install a video alarm system.

We would have to make a choice. Which option should we support? People have different views about the best ways of combating crime. But whichever way we choose, the skills and knowledge of design and technology will always be needed.

3 If you were in charge of a group with £5000 to spend on preventing crime how would you spend it? Write down some ideas and the reasons for your final choice.

4 Look back at the list you made of crimes in order of seriousness. Does this list fit in with how you decided to use the money?

Written with the help of INTERMEDIATE TECHNOLOGY

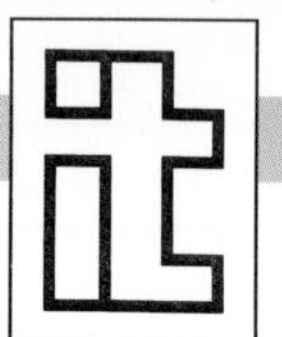

3 Winners and losers- fish processing in Lake Victoria

The introduction of new technology to the fishing industry of Lake Victoria in Africa has created gains for some and losses for others

Fishing has always been a very important part of people's lives along the shores of Lake Victoria in Africa. Traditionally women have caught many varieties of fish with traps or basket scoops woven from papyrus, tree bark, creepers and banana fibres. The most popular fish is *enkejje*. Today this traditional equipment has been largely replaced with modern fishing technology. The women no longer fish, but they still process and preserve fish by smoking or drying.

Pause for thought
Which types of fish do people in Britain eat? Where are these fish caught?

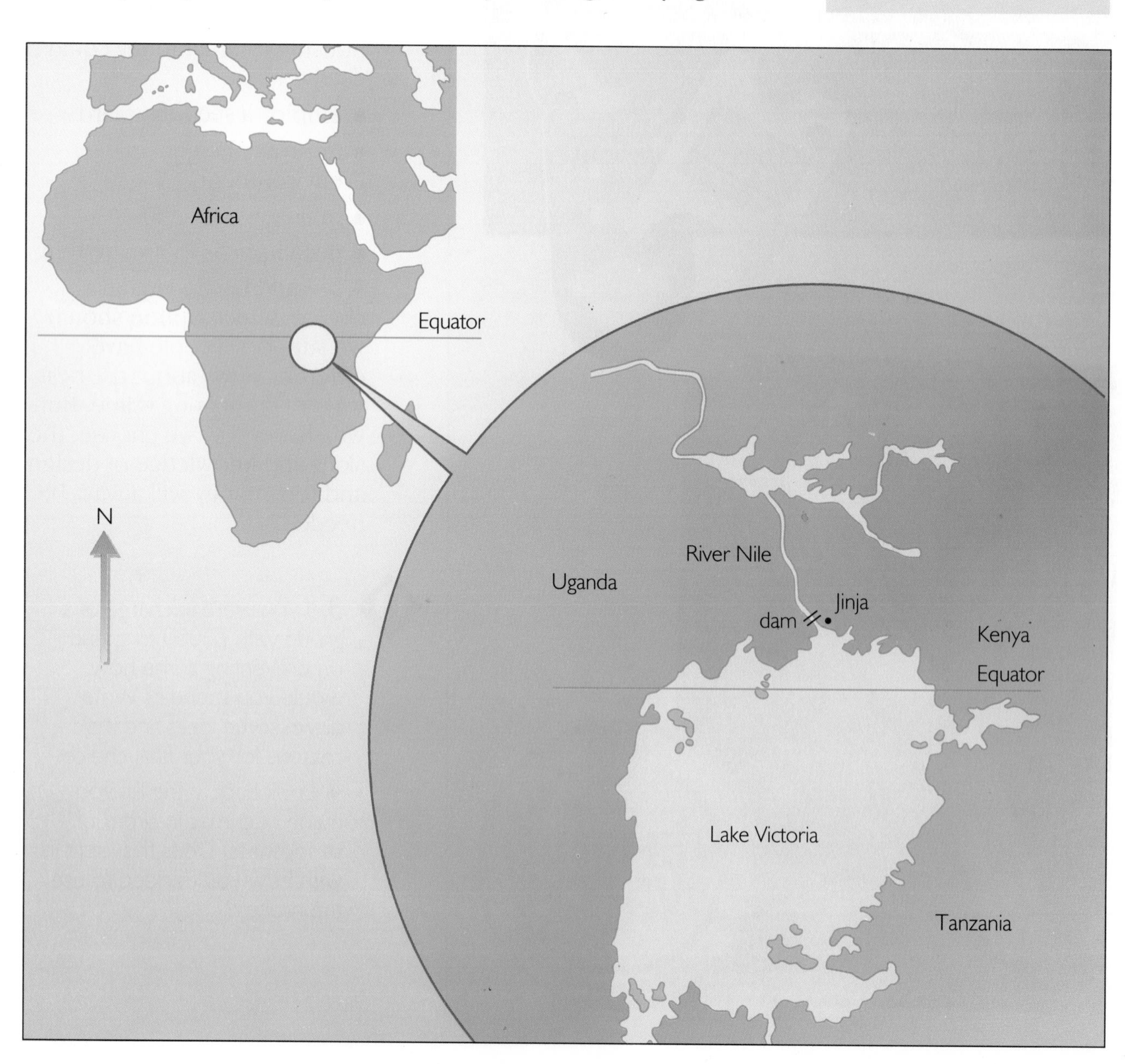

Enkejje – a food for children

Enkejje is a small fish usually eaten whole, like the British eat sardines or whitebait. It is very rich in protein and calcium. It is also low in fat, but provides just the level essential for children's development. It is a very important children's food for two reasons:

▲ *The* enkejje *fish of Lake Victoria.*

- The low fat content makes *enkejje* easy to digest. In Britain, low-fat white fish such as plaice are often given to people who are ill for the same reason.
- The protein helps to limit the effects of diseases such as measles. These are most dangerous when a child is malnourished.

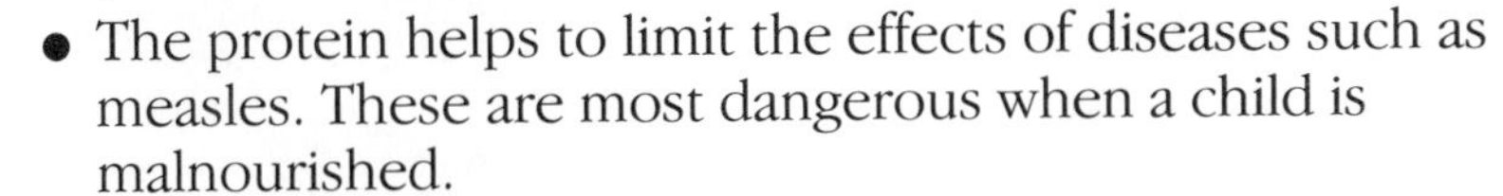

The women are well aware of this and feed their youngsters with *enkejje*.

Protein	56%
Calcium	8%
Fat	11%

▲ *The nutritional composition of* enkejje.

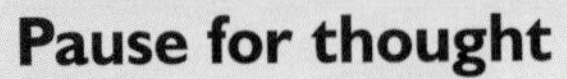

Pause for thought
What types of foods do people in Britain give to their children? Why might a child's diet be different from an adult's?

Drying the fish

Because they are low in fat, *enkejje* are easy to dry in the sun. The fish are speared together on sticks like kebabs and then spread out on clean rocks. They are covered with grasses to keep off the dirt and the direct heat of the sun. The rocks heat up during the day and the drying process continues at night as the heat is radiated back from the rock surface. The dried fish can be kept for a long time.

The people living around Lake Victoria had developed a technology for catching and using *enkejje*. However, this way of meeting their need for food was changed by decisions made many kilometres away.

▲ Enkejje *laid out to dry.*

Research
Find out what other types of food can be preserved by drying.

A new arrival – the Nile perch

▲ *The Nile perch introduced into the lake by the government. It is much bigger than the* enkejje.

Some years ago the Ugandan Government and foreign fisheries experts introduced into Lake Victoria two species of fish from the River Nile: the Nile perch and the tilapia. They wanted to increase the catch of these fish from the lake so that they could export them. They have been successful, but at a price. While the catch of Nile fish has increased by leaps and bounds, the catch of *enkejje* has fallen to almost nothing.

Pause for thought
Who else should have been consulted? Why? Why do you think the people are not catching as many *enkejje*?

The government had thought it a good idea to breed the Nile perch in Lake Victoria. The increased yield of these valuable fish could be exported to other countries to bring in much needed income for the country. However, the government had not realized how it would affect the *enkejje* and the local people:

- The Nile fish have eaten the *enkejje* until they are almost extinct.
- Lake Victoria is being suffocated by algae, which used to be eaten by *enkejje*. Many other fish are dying as a result of the algae.
- The local people do not like to eat the Nile perch and the fish are too oily to give to young children.
- The Nile perch are too oily to be dried in the sun. They must be dried in special ovens which cause pollution in the area.

1 Make a list of who gains and who loses, directly and indirectly, from the introduction of the Nile fish into Lake Victoria.

2 How do they gain or lose?

The local women respond

The women of the Jinja district, bordering the lake, responded to these problems in several ways. *Enkejje* are scarce now, but the women found that if they pound and sieve the whole *enkejje* fish to a fine powder it can be stored and mixed with baby food to make it more nutritious. This idea has been copied commercially, and is promoted by government health clinics. The women also want to establish separate fish ponds where they can farm *enkejje*. The Minister of Agriculture has now stepped in. She has banned the use of small-holed fishing nets in the lake to try to save those *enkejje* that remain. With larger holes in these modern nets only the larger species are caught.

▲ *Nile perch can grow as big as people!*

Pause for thought

The introduction of any new technology always brings advantages and disadvantages, **winners** and **losers**. Can you think of other examples where new technology has produced gains for one group of people and losses for another?

4 Measuring fitness with new technology

New technology helps doctors to diagnose and treat patients with heart and lung disease

We are all concerned about health these days. More and more people are eating healthier foods and taking regular exercise. But heart disease is still a major illness and many thousands of people die from it each year. However, with regular check-ups and treatment there is no reason why someone with heart disease should not enjoy a full and active life.

Hospitals use a wide range of equipment to diagnose and treat disease. Some designs are very old – the stethoscope is hundreds of years old. Hospitals also use the latest technologies to help them provide the best care for their patients.

▲ *More and more people are running in marathons.*

1 Look at the photograph opposite of a patient being treated in a hospital. List the equipment that you can recognize.

2 Is there any equipment that you do not recognize? What do you think it is for?

Designers of medical equipment have developed computer-based systems which doctors can use to check people's fitness by measuring their responses to exercise.

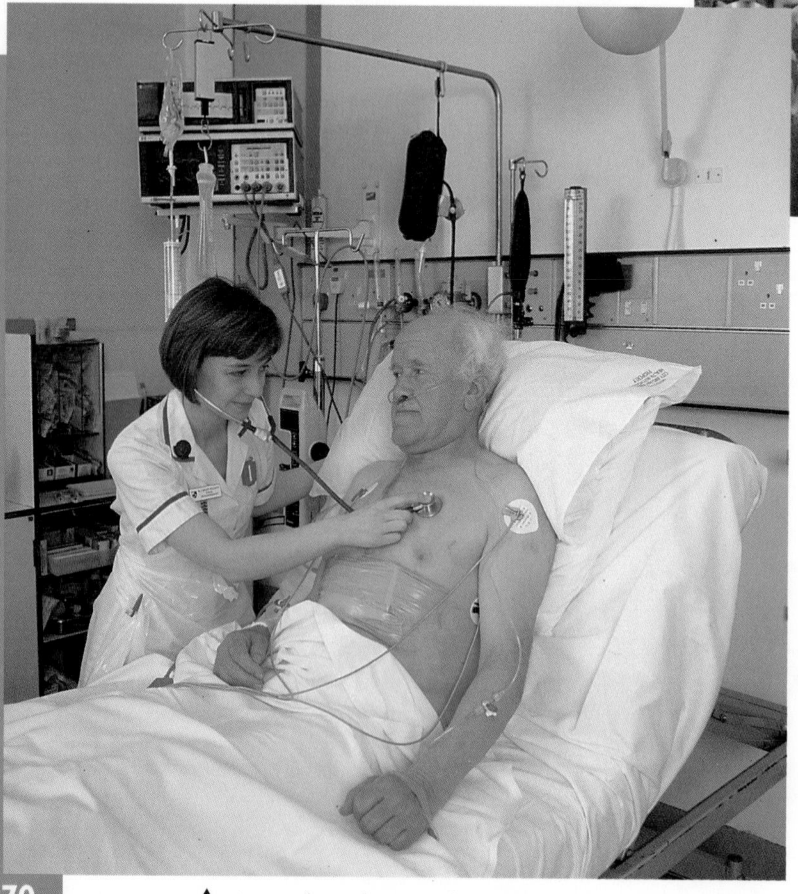

▲ *A modern hospital cardiac unit.*

Types of exercise

There are two main types of exercise. A person taking part in an **aerobic** exercise such as running, swimming, walking or cycling breathes throughout the exercise. During **anaerobic** exercises such as weight-lifting or sprinting the person does not breathe until the end of the exercise.

Both types of exercise use muscles. Muscles need fuel, in the form of food, and oxygen to 'burn' this fuel. It is the heart's job to provide muscles with a regular supply of food and oxygen.

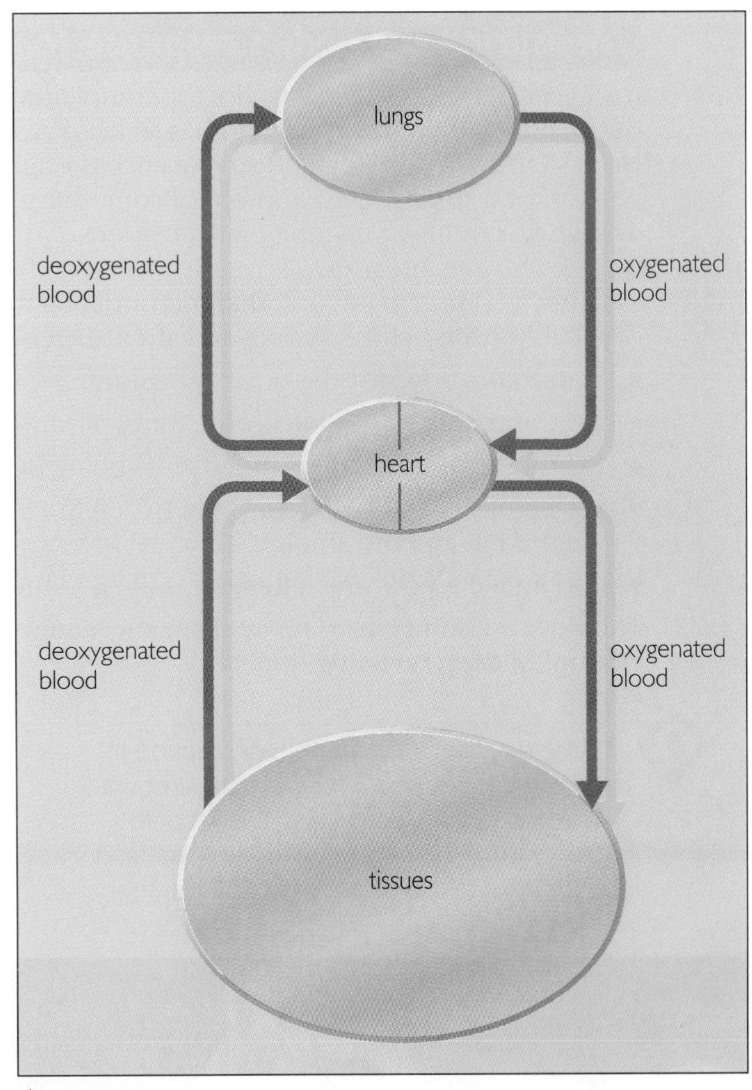

▲ *The blood circulation system.*

The heart

The heart is a pump made of muscle. You can hear and feel it pumping. It pumps blood carrying food and oxygen around the body. When we take exercise we can feel our body's response to the exercise.

Pause for thought
What happens to your heart rate and breathing when you start to exercise? What happens when you stop exercising?

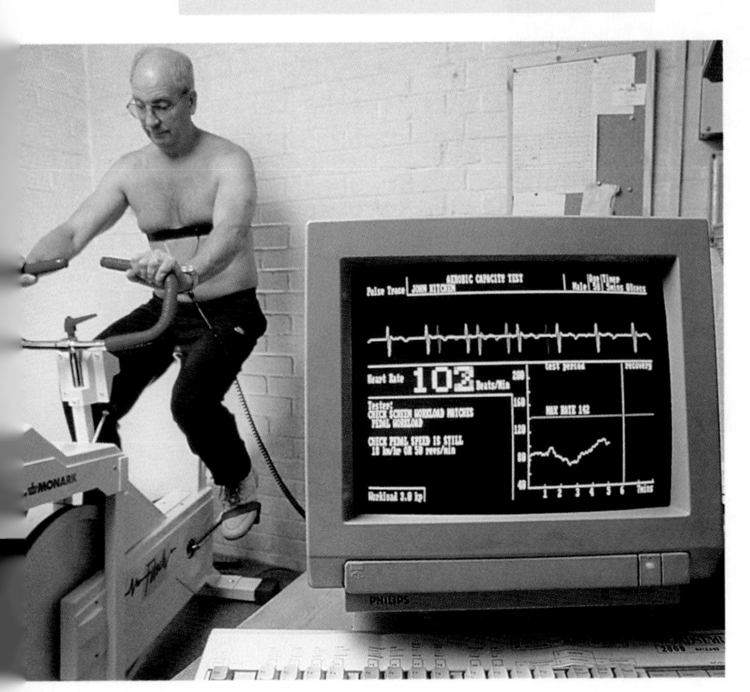

Why measure responses to exercise?

Exercise testing is used for various purposes:

- Athletes training for a competition want to know when they have reached their peak fitness.
- Doctors test patients to diagnose disease.
- Patients recovering from disease need to know how they are progressing.
- Doctors who have developed a new exercise programme might test patients before and after exercise to see if it has made any difference.

Any machine or system used for exercise testing needs to allow for all these possible uses. The next part of this Case Study will look at how a real system is used.

Measuring the body's response to exercise

A 55-year-old man goes to his doctor complaining that he gets out of breath climbing stairs and has to keep stopping for a rest. He is slightly overweight and smokes occasionally. He might just be unfit or it might be a symptom of something more serious. The doctor wants to test the man's response to exercise to find out why he gets breathless so easily.

To get a complete picture, the doctor needs to measure each of the following before, during and after exercise:

- heart rate – how fast the heart is beating;
- breathing rate – how quickly the lungs are moving in and out;
- breathing volumes – how much air is being breathed in;
- oxygen uptake – the difference between the amount of oxygen breathed in and the amount of oxygen breathed out;
- food intake – how much fuel the body is using.

The doctor also needs to relate these measurements to the amount of exercise being done.

1 Use sketches and a written description to explain how you could measure the amount of exercise someone is doing. How could you measure the person's breathing rate and the amount of air breathed in and out?

In the past each of these measurements would have been made separately. The heart rate would be measured by feeling the pulse and using a stop-watch. Oxygen levels would be measured in a laboratory. This would take time and require a lot of medical and technical staff. The patient would have to wait a long time for the results of the test.

Now patients can benefit from the new system which can measure all these quantities at the same time. The system uses a computer so the results can be compared easily with those of other people of the same age, sex and weight. The computer also stores the results so that the doctor can check whether the patient's condition is getting better or worse.

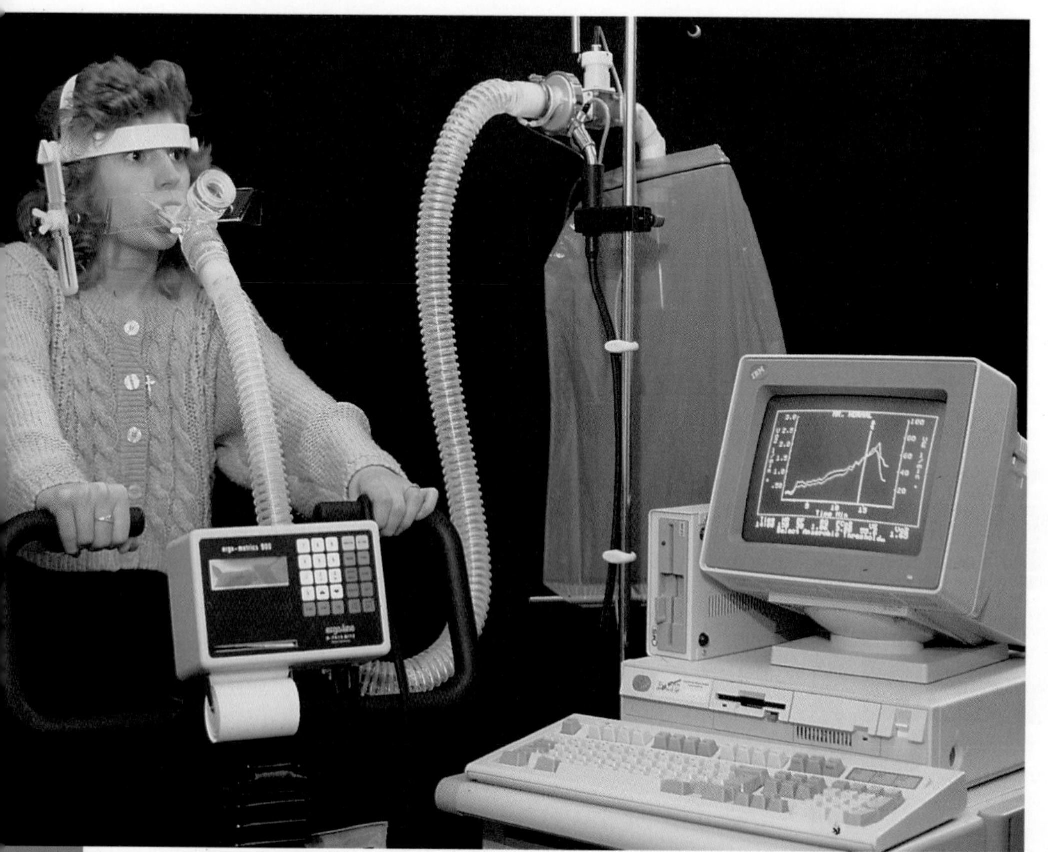

▲ *A new computer-based system for measuring responses to exercise.*

Pause for thought

What are the advantages of this type of system?

The patient's results

How did the patient perform? This type of test can show whether the patient has heart or lung disease which might cause breathlessness.

During the patient's exercise test:

- his breathing became faster and deeper;
- the level of oxygen being absorbed by his lungs increased;
- his heart rate only increased very slightly.

He had eaten so there was no shortage of energy.

Pause for thought
Look at the patient's responses to exercise. Are any of them unusual?

▲ *Now they have the results they can plan how to make him better.*

What do these results mean?

The patient's blood, which contains oxygen breathed into the lungs, is not being pumped around the body quickly enough to meet the demands of the muscles. This is why he has to stop after very little exercise. This means he probably has heart disease. With care and treatment he can lead a normal life. Without exercise response testing he might have been unaware of his condition until something serious happened. His results are stored by the computer and the doctor will be able to see how he responds to treatment.

▲ *Prevention is better than cure: the Health Education Council promotes ways in which we can all become healthier.*

Written with the help of INTERMEDIATE TECHNOLOGY

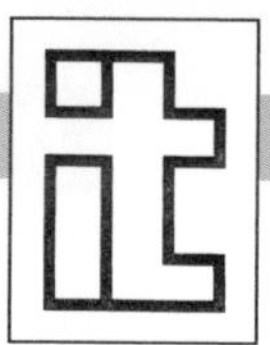

5 Preserving skills – food technology in Sri Lanka

A group of women in Sri Lanka use their knowledge of food preservation techniques to develop products for sale

Many foods go bad if they are not correctly processed, packaged and stored. They can taste unpleasant and are sometimes dangerous to eat. If fruit is left in a warm place for some time it soon begins to smell bad and has to be thrown away.

All over the world, people have developed different ways of preserving fresh foods to prevent waste. Preservation techniques include:

- drying;
- smoking;
- adding salt;
- adding vinegar;
- adding sugar.

These methods work by stopping micro-organisms living and growing. Salt and drying, for example, reduce the amount of water in the food so that micro-organisms cannot live. Vinegar makes the food too acidic for micro-organisms.

▲ *All these preserved foods are found in the supermarket.*

Research

Go to your local supermarket and find foods which have been preserved by each of the methods listed here. Produce a table like this:

Method	Food
Drying Smoking	Apricots, currants

Why preserve food?

Food is preserved for two main reasons:

- **To provide food security** – Foods are preserved when there is a lot of them, for example after a harvest. They can then be eaten at other times of the year when there is a shortage.
- **To add variety to the diet** – For example, fruit and vegetables are often made into pickles, chutneys and sauces. These add interest and flavour to food and provide a range of important vitamins and minerals.

The basic methods of food preservation are the same all over the world. However, there are differences in the type of ingredients used, the equipment and resources available and the people's preferences.

Fruit leathers

Drying has been used for a long time to preserve food. For as long as records have been kept, people have dried their crops in the sun.

In parts of India mango pulp is mixed with sugar, poured into a tray and placed in the sun to dry. The result is a dry pliable sheet which is cut into strips and then eaten as a sweet. This **fruit leather** is popular with people of many ages, particularly children who often eat it for a snack. In many other parts of the world people make similar products. In Britain raspberries can be preserved in the same way.

Research

Can you buy some of these products (they may even be called fruit leathers) locally? If possible, taste them and see if you like them.

▲ *Fruit leathers made by drying fruit are popular snacks in India. We can buy similar products in Britain.*

Food preservation at home

In some societies people do not preserve food as much as they used to. Why do you think this is? You could ask elderly people for their views. How much food preservation people do at home depends upon:

- how much surplus food is available;
- how much spare time people have;
- whether people can afford to buy the ingredients needed, such as vinegar or sugar;
- other costs, such as fuel for cooking;
- whether people have the necessary equipment.

For some people it is more convenient to buy preserved foods, especially if they are reasonably priced.

The story that follows describes how a group of women in Sri Lanka used traditional technology and local knowledge to produce and sell a range of preserved fruit products.

Women producers

Moneragala is a small rural town in the south-east of Sri Lanka. During much of the year there is a surplus of fruit which is sold at low prices or simply left to rot on the roadside.

A group of women decided to take advantage of this cheap fruit by producing a range of jams, chutneys and pickles. A speciality would be *lunu dehi*, a traditional lime pickle eaten regularly with the main meal of rice and curried vegetables. Using preservation skills, learned from their mothers and grandmothers, the women began production. People would only continue to buy their products if the quality was always good, so they developed simple tests to check factors such as

- consistency;
- colour;
- flavour.

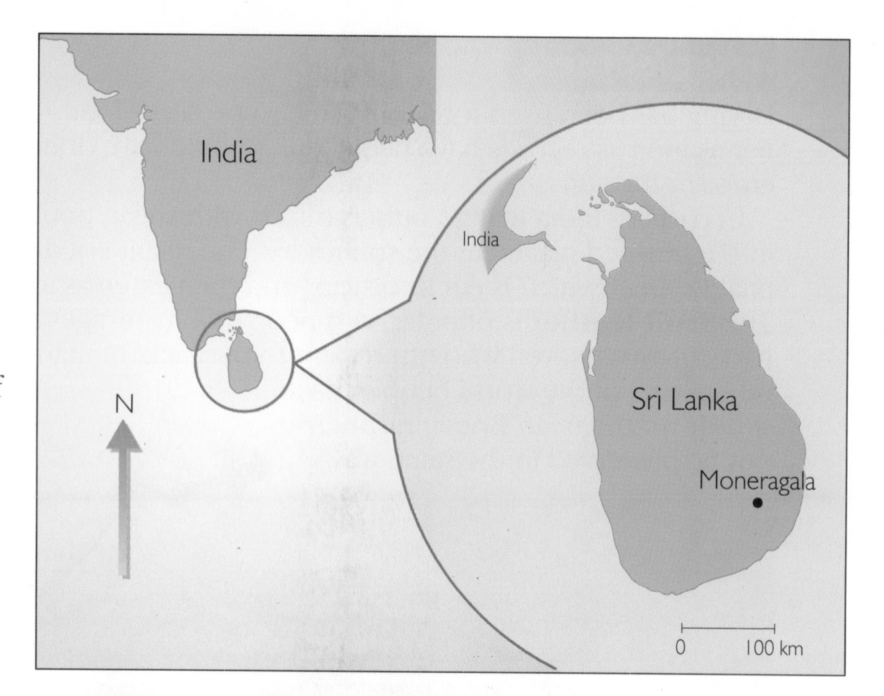

What to produce?

Before making a product for sale it is important to carry out **market research**, to find out what people need and why. The women did this by:

- looking at the products already being sold in the shops;
- talking to local shopkeepers to find out what products sold best;
- talking to local people to find out what fruit products they bought.

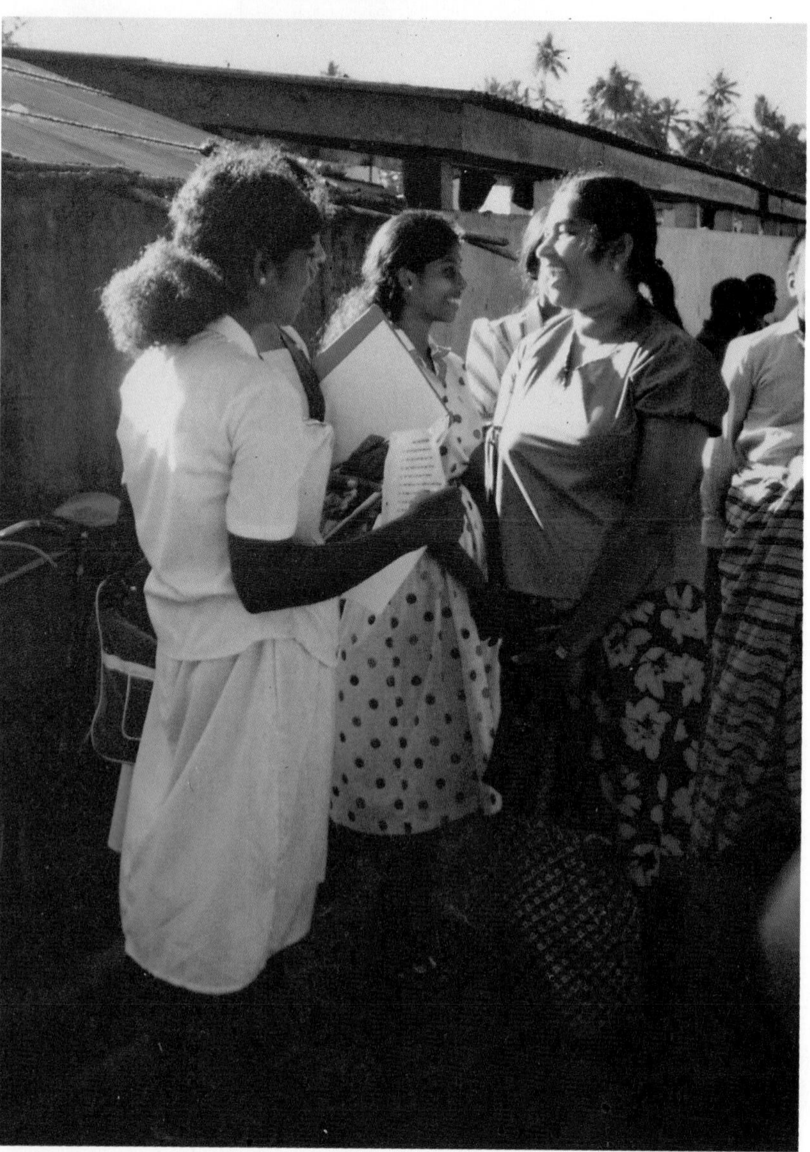

▲ *Market research to find out what customers want.*

From their research the women learnt that local people wanted products which were cheap and sold in small quantities. Instead of the standard glass jar which the larger manufacturers used, they decided to use polythene bags and small plastic pots.

The women did not have any special sealing equipment so they used what they had. To seal the plastic bags they used a metal blade heated with a candle. Each pot was sealed by laying a thin sheet of plastic over the top. This was then heat-sealed with an iron filled with burning coconut husks.

▲ *Filling the pots.*

The products were sold at local 'polas', open market-places where people come to buy and sell goods.

Many groups of people world-wide try to make and sell new products from a glut of fruit. Very few are successful because many do not take into account the needs of the consumer. The women in Moneragala were successful because they carried out market research and made products and packages to suit the needs of the local people.

1 Imagine that you have a garden full of fruit and vegetables. If you decided to preserve the produce for sale, what things would you consider carefully before beginning?

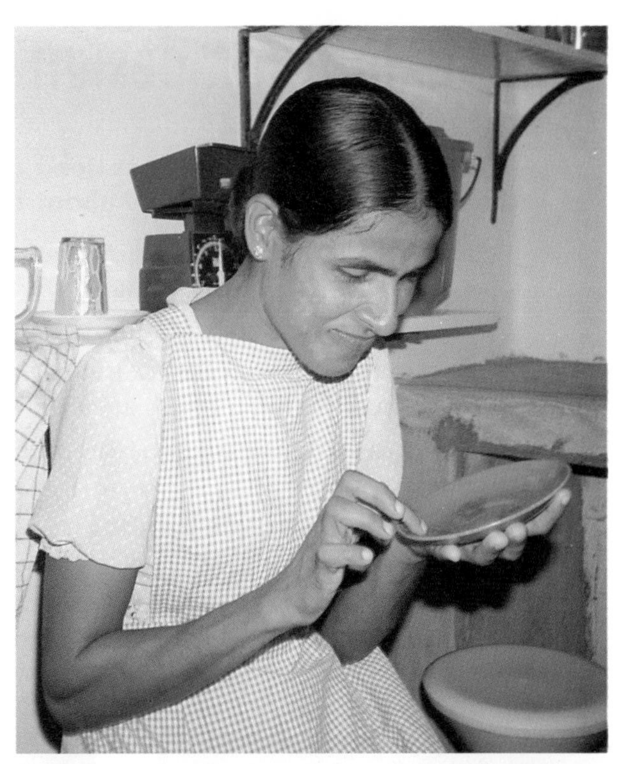

▲ *Testing the product to see whether it will set.*

Pause for thought

Why might people want to buy food in small quantities? What foods are sold in small packages in Britain?

▲ *Sealing the plastic bags.*

6 Exhibition design – getting a message across

What do exhibition designers need to think about when producing a design and how do they go about their work?

You have seen the work of an exhibition designer if you have:

- visited a museum (like Jorvik, the Museum of the Moving Image, Beamish or the Imperial War Museum);
- been to an exhibition or theme park (like the Age of Chivalry, the Canterbury Experience, Disney World or the Last Labyrinth);
- been to a trade fair (like the Clothes Show, the Motor Show or a county show);
- visited an information display (on road safety, staying healthy or not wasting energy).

All the work in this Case Study has been carried out by students on a course in Museum and Exhibition Design Studies at Humberside Polytechnic.

▲ *Some different approaches to exhibition design.*

What are exhibitions for?

Exhibitions are all about **communicating information**, **presenting a point of view** or **persuading people**. They must gain the visitors' attention and make them want to find out more. Visitors should leave the exhibition having enjoyed themselves as well as knowing more about the subject.

Pause for thought
Think about the exhibitions you have visited. What did you like about them? Who do you think the exhibitions were aimed at?

Different kinds of exhibitions

- **Launching a new product** – The display shown on the right is part of an exhibition designed to tell you about a new edition of A A Milne's books. The designer has used the author's most famous character, Winnie the Pooh, to catch your eye.

▲ *This display uses large card cut-outs.*

▲ *This display deals with a controversial issue.*

- **Persuading people** – This design work shown on the left is for an exhibition about HIV and AIDS. Several methods are used to make the information interesting, and to help the visitor understand the message.

  The designer has suggested part of a circle of figures, including some which are just wire frames. The circle is completed by reflections in mirrored panels. If you stand in one of the frames, your reflection helps complete the circle to make you think about who might be affected by HIV.

▲ *Each room in the exhibition says something different about the rainforest.*

- **Giving information on conservation** – This design is for a museum exhibition about life in a tropical rainforest. As you walk through the rooms of the exhibition, you will see displays showing different aspects of the rainforest. For each aspect there are displays around the walls and on special screens. They include: display cases showing what the rainforest looks like; photographs and videos about the animal and plant life; cut-away shapes and display boards to transform the rooms into a 'forest'; written information panels.

▲ *This exhibition will show where Charlie Chaplin worked as well as what he did.*

- **Helping to explain the past** – The designs on the left are for an exhibition about the life and work of the film actor Charlie Chaplin. The ideas include: scenes from his films, with dummies and props; the costumes he wore; information about his films and the film studios he worked in.

- **Giving information about a company or business –** Businesses often need to explain who they are, what they do and how they developed, perhaps to get money from banks or shareholders, or at trade fairs in other countries. Laura Ashley is a business designing, producing and selling clothes and home furnishings. This exhibition plan includes a shop for selling Laura Ashley products and access details such as sloping floors and emergency exits.

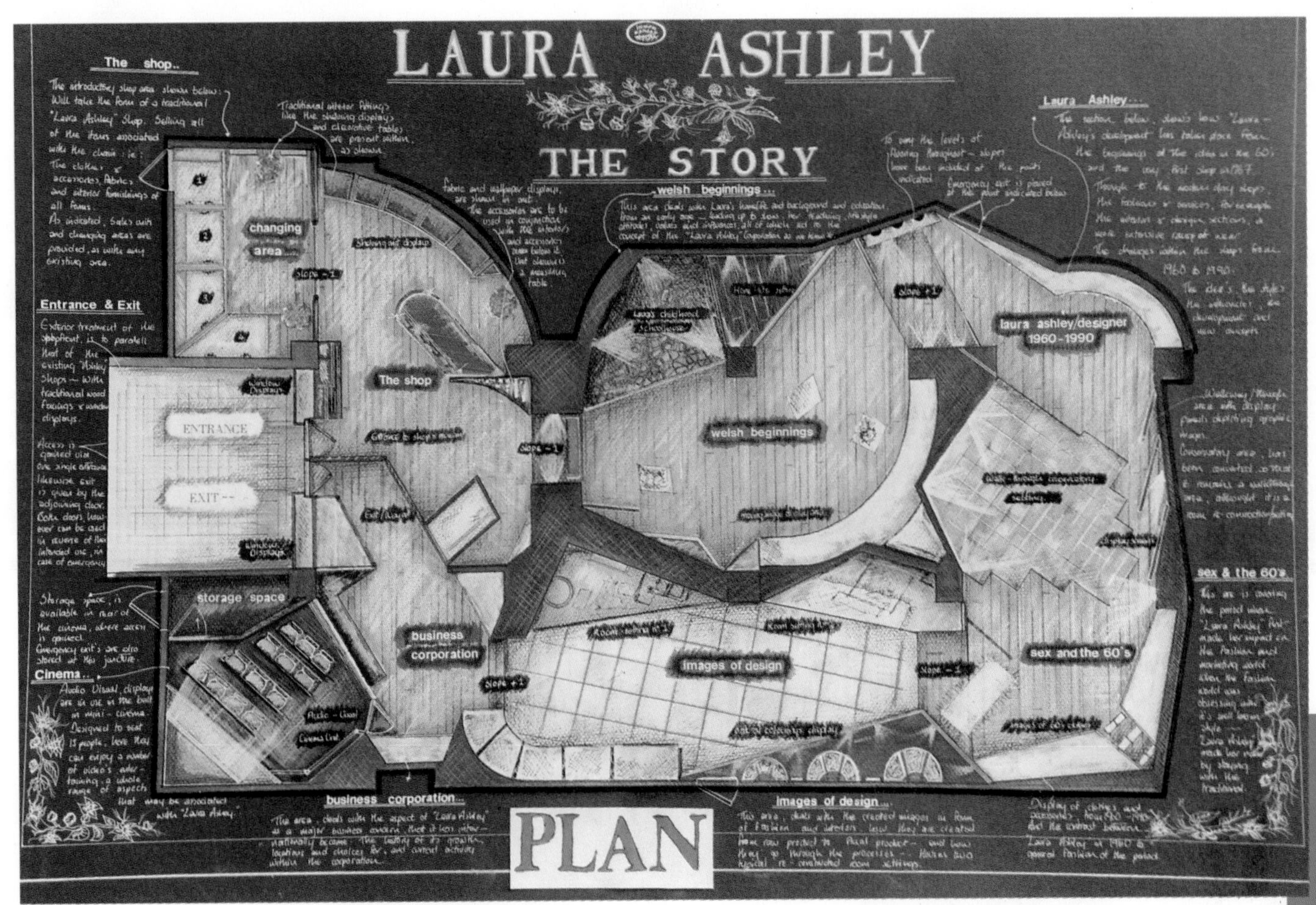

▲ *This exhibition will tell the story of business success.*

1 Look back at each of these designs for exhibitions. Are they all aimed at the same people or are some of them designed for a specific audience?

2 Which things do all the designs have in common?

3 Can you see any features which are unique to one of the designs?

4 Use your answers to these questions to produce a checklist of things to think about when you design an exhibition or a display.

The next part of this Case Study looks at the steps followed by a student designing an exhibition display.

Developing a display

The student has been working on a design for an exhibition about the last ten years of children's book publishing. He designs it using **three-dimensional modelling.**

The design is based on large book shapes, standing up and lying flat, open and shut. The early models have pages or pictures falling out of them, like playing cards.

Once the student is happy with his idea, he goes on to make a small-scale model including all the detail that will be used in the final display. He uses accurately scaled-down shapes and sizes and exact colours.

▲ *Some early 3D models.*

Finally, he builds a full-size display. Sometimes things that seem fine on a small-scale model do not work when you make the final version.

▲ *A detailed small-scale model.*

▲ *The final display.* ▶

1 This student used 3D modelling to develop his design. Where else might a designer prefer to use modelling rather than drawing?

2 What advantages does 3D modelling have over drawing as a way of designing? When might it be better to use drawing?

We have seen how a design technologist produced an exhibition to display other people's work. Sometimes design technologists need to produce displays and exhibitions of their own work. A group of architects might want to show designs for a new building to a client, or a group wanting financial backing might need to explain their ideas to a bank. Often you will have to explain your work to others. These examples should help you.

7 Printing technology – from wood-blocks to computers

The development of printing is a good example of how technological advance has enabled people to meet changing needs

We are surrounded by printed materials such as posters, leaflets, tickets and decorated T-shirts. Printed words and pictures fill books, comics and magazines.

Why printing?

The Chinese were probably the first people to use printing, around AD 500.

Before the development of printing in China, all books and documents were written by hand. This was the task of a **scribe**. If several copies of something were needed, scribes would have to write it out over and over again.

The Emperor of China and other influential people needed written documents to govern the country. Merchants needed to record their transactions. Holy books were in great demand. The scribes could not keep up with demand! A faster way of making lots of copies of important documents had to be found.

Research

Apart from printing, the Chinese were responsible for a number of other important inventions. Find out what you can about the others.

The first idea

Rich people used to use a seal to put their mark or signature onto documents. Hot wax was dripped onto the paper and then the seal was pressed into the wax to leave an impression. The idea of printing may have come from this because the Chinese word for seal is 'yin' and this is also the word they use for 'print'. If a seal was inked, it could be used to put an impression on paper without the use of wax.

▲ *Applying a wax seal.*

Wood-block printing

Early Chinese printing involved the use of wood-blocks. They carved their writing on the blocks, making the characters they wanted to print stand out. The wood carver had to carve the words backwards so they would be the right way round when printed.

The printer inked the raised parts of the wood-block and pressed a sheet of paper onto the inked surface. The paper was smoothed with a soft brush and then peeled off the block to reveal the printed impression. Finally, the paper was hung up to dry and the block inked again to repeat the process.

The Chinese became experts at this form of printing. The wood-blocks became larger and the carvings more detailed and intricate. They could even print complex pictures.

This process meant that many copies of documents and books could be produced relatively quickly, but whole pages had to be carved at one time and each block could only be used to print the same page over and over again.

▲ *A wooden printing block from Japan made in the 16th century.*

Pause for thought

What problems can you see with this method of printing? How would you solve these problems?

On pages 86–9 we look at how some of these problems were solved.

Movable type

In the eleventh century a Chinese man, Bi Sheng, had the idea of printing with **movable** type. He used clay instead of wood. He cut the clay to form individual characters and then fired them to make them hard. To print something he arranged the characters (or **type**) that he needed in an iron frame. When the frame was full, he inked it in the same way as a wood-block and used it to print onto a sheet of paper. Multiple copies could be made by re-inking the type. When he had enough copies, the characters could be rearranged in the frame to print something else.

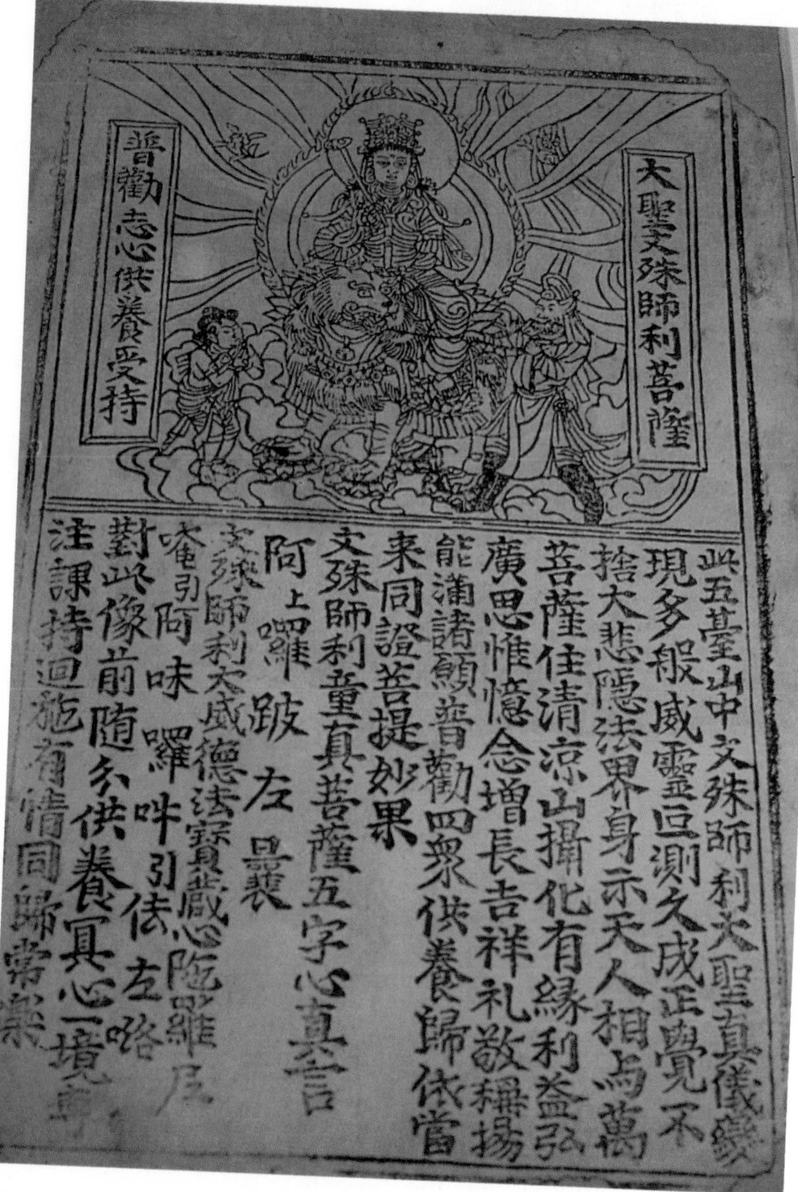

▲ *Chinese writing is not suitable for movable type.*

Research

Make a list of all the characters needed for printing in English. Do not forget punctuation marks such as commas and full-stops. Would printing have been easier using our alphabet?

Find out about another alphabet, such as Arabic, Greek or Russian. How many characters would be needed to print in that language?

This was a major step forward, but it did not replace the old systems of block printing and scribing. The Chinese language has thousands of different characters – you can see some of them above. This made it difficult for printers to make type for each one.

Printing in Europe

The idea of printing may have been brought to Europe by travellers who had visited China or by the popularity of playing cards during the fourteenth century. Cards had been printed with wood-blocks in China since the tenth century. When people started buying the Chinese cards in Europe, they may also have found out how they were printed.

Pause for thought

Why do you think the process of printing took so long to reach Europe?

In medieval Britain, the Church was the centre of learning. All early books were religious and were written in Latin, French or Greek. Books were still written by hand by monks and were often decorated with beautiful pictures. These were called **illuminated manuscripts**. It could take a scribe up to eighteen months to produce a Bible. Because the process was so slow and because so few people could write books, they were extremely expensive. Only the very rich could afford to buy books and most were owned by the Church.

▲ *In medieval Britain monks known as scribes copied Bibles and other religious books by hand.*

Research

Visit a local museum and look at some early books and illuminated manuscripts. Find out when they were produced and how long it took.

By the fourteenth century, non-religious books were being written in Europe. Writers also began to use their own country's language, for example *The Canterbury Tales* by Geoffrey Chaucer.

▲ *An illuminated manuscript produced by a scribe. Imagine how long it would take to produce just one book like this by hand.*

Pause for thought

Were the reasons for the development of printing in Europe the same as those in China? Was the invention of printing inevitable?

A growing demand

As more Europeans learned to read and write, the demand for books increased. Block printing was used to print pictures of saints to sell to pilgrims who could not afford hand-painted pictures.

A shorter Bible was printed for churchmen who could not afford a hand-written volume. Cutting wood-blocks was an extremely slow process, so a quicker way of mass-producing books had to be found.

Movable type in Europe

By the fifteenth century, people in Europe began to experiment with movable type. A German, Johann Gutenberg, a merchant and goldsmith, is thought to have developed the first successful system. He used moulds to make sets of identical metal blocks each with a single raised letter of the alphabet on it. He also developed a new kind of ink suited to metal rather than wood. The individual pieces of metal type were arranged in a frame for printing. The pieces could be used again and again. With this new technique he printed the famous Gutenberg Bible.

▲ *A print-shop in the fifteenth century. In the background men are sorting out the type pieces needed from big trays of type.*

▲ *Thousands of pieces of metal type were used in a traditional printing works, with letters and numbers in all sorts of different styles and sizes.*

The process was quick to catch on. European languages have far fewer symbols than Chinese so Gutenberg's method was extremely successful. Demand for printed material grew as books became more readily available and cheaper.

After the invention of this new type of printing, Europeans could obtain copies of old texts, but there was also a demand for new and original material. Information could be spread quickly to large numbers of people and this led to the birth of the newspaper and **mass communication.**

Mechanical presses

As demand grew, so printing technology needed to improve. Mechanical presses were invented during the nineteenth century that could print far more quickly than hand-operated ones. Developments in the typesetting process were also taking place.

In the first half of the twentieth century, the popularity of newspapers was at its height. They were read in virtually every home. However, by the end of the 1960s, changes in the way we live meant that fewer people were buying newspapers.

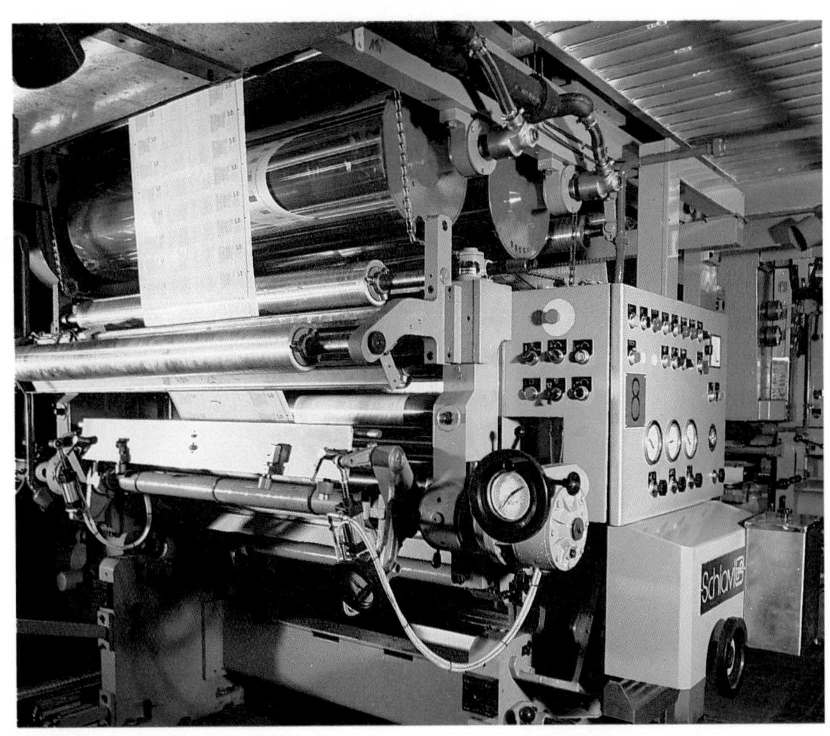

▲ *This newspaper press can print, collate and fold thousands of newspapers every hour.*

Pause for thought
What were these 'changes in the way we live'? What other developments in communication were taking place at this time?

Research
Many different methods of printing have been developed. Find out about one and produce a display describing how it works.

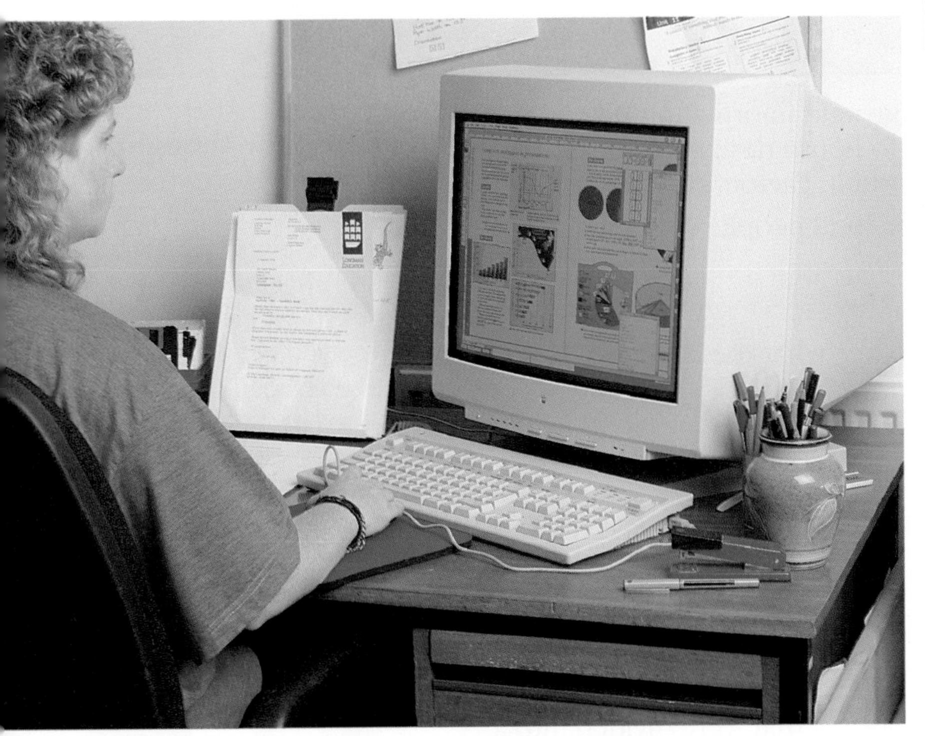

▲ *A computerized desk-top publishing system can produce pages of text and pictures laid out ready for printing.*

Printing today

Just as the printing press was developed to solve the medieval scribes' problems, so advances in technology enable newspapers to compete with the other means of mass communication today. Advances in electronics and computers mean that mass communication is faster and covers larger distances than were thought possible a century ago.

Pause for thought
How have computers changed printing techniques?

Written with the help of INTERMEDIATE TECHNOLOGY

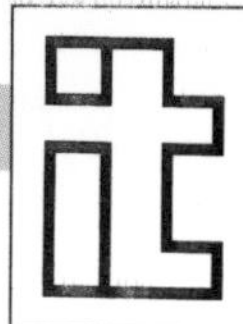

8 Designing houses to suit people's needs

Two housing projects in Peru show how important it can be to involve local people in making design decisions

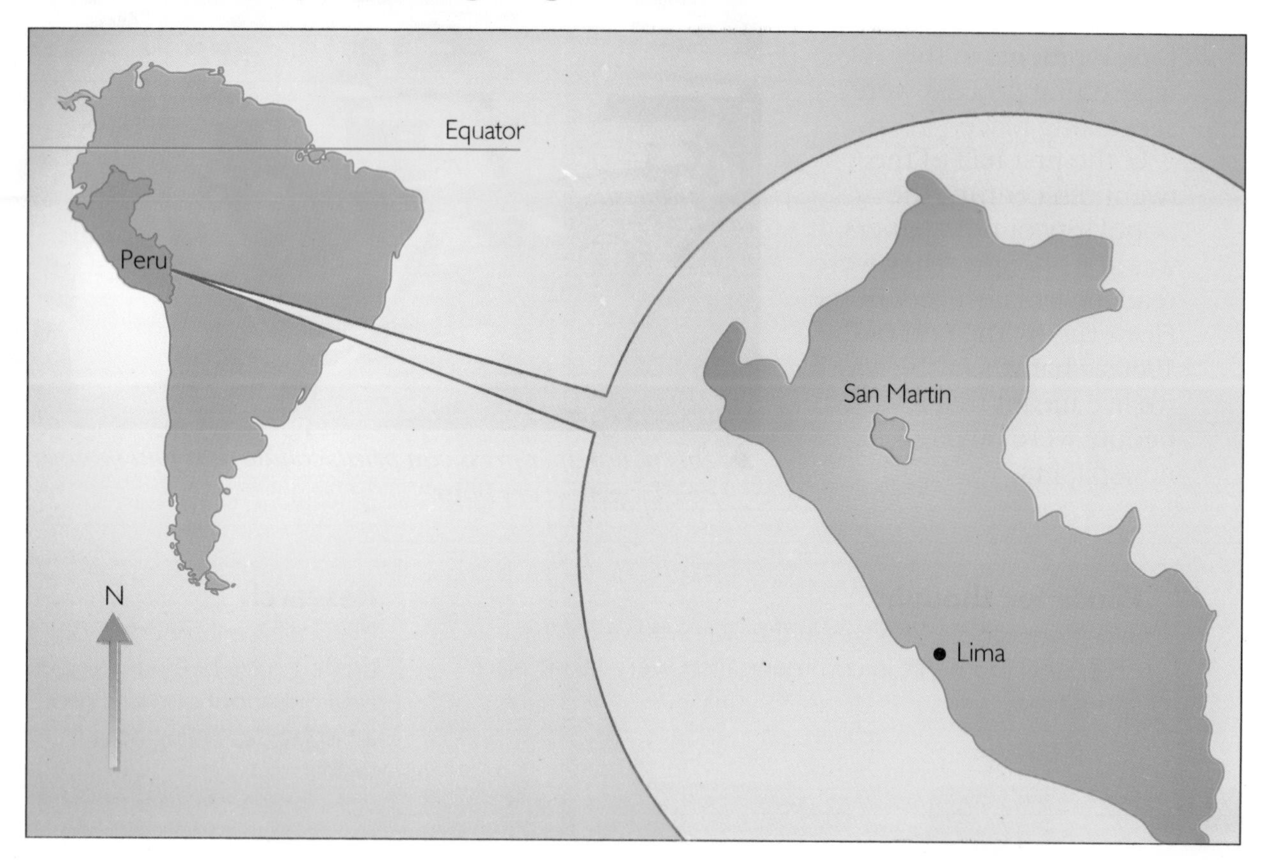

Designers need to gather background information before they start on a design project. To house designers, for example, **local knowledge** is very important. Factors such as:

- the needs and lifestyles of the local people;
- the weather conditions;
- the materials available;
- whether people can afford to buy what the designers are producing;

all have to be researched.

Pause for thought
What might go wrong if designers do not talk to the people who will use what they are designing? How would you find out whether people need or could afford something that you are designing?

Getting it wrong

In Peru, as in many countries, houses are built as part of overseas aid projects. After an earthquake in 1970, several houses were built in Nepena, a town in Peru, with the help of an aid agency. The local people were not asked about the type of homes they wanted. The aid workers built houses that were divided into a number of small rooms and were at one end of the plots of land.

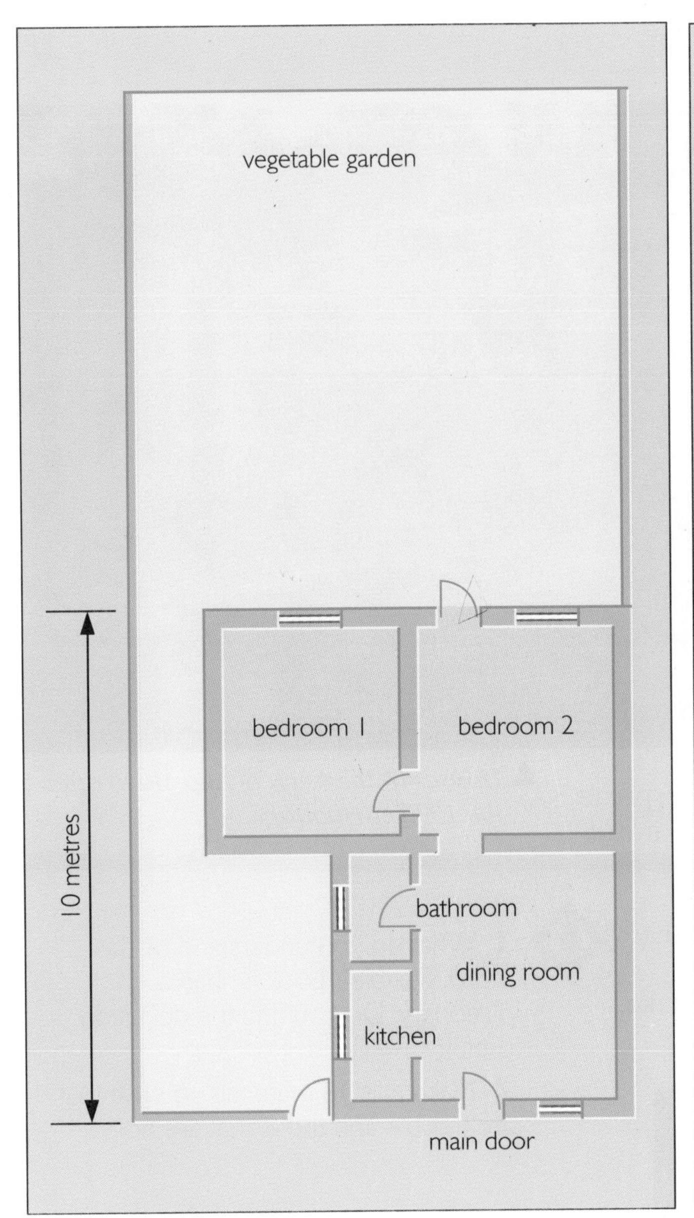

▲ *A floor plan of one of the houses built by aid workers.*

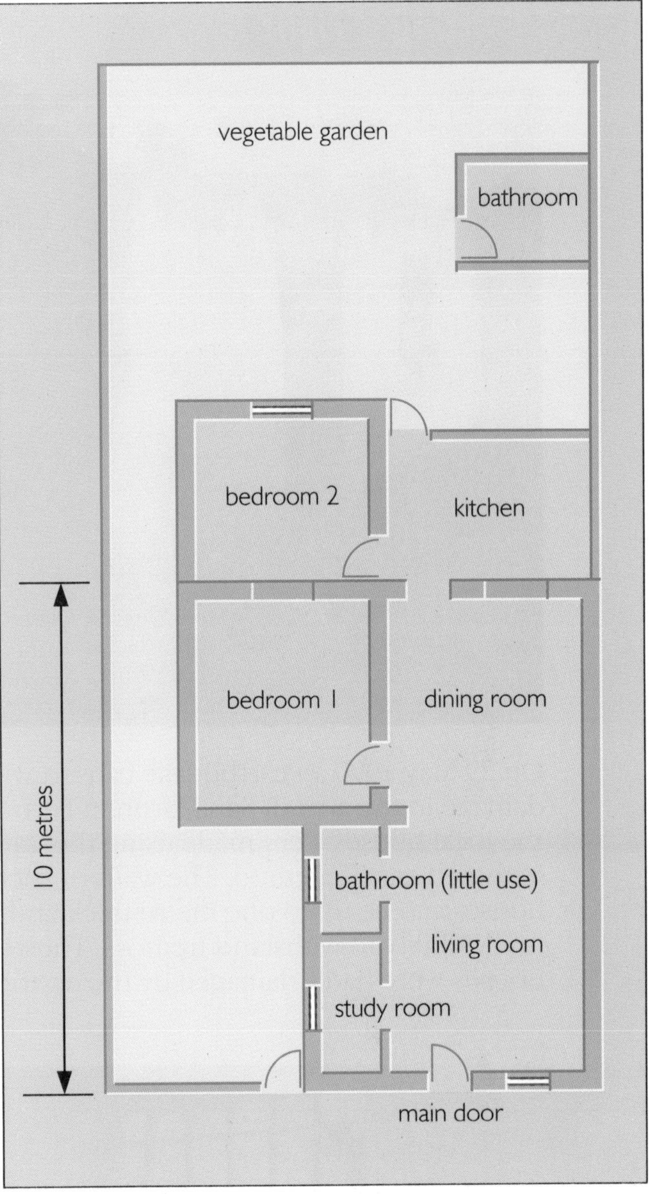

▲ *The floor plan after residents had redesigned a house.*

After the houses were built and contracts signed, people moved in. They changed the houses into the homes they wanted by knocking down walls and relocating the kitchens. If the designers had consulted the people about what they wanted all this extra work could have been avoided.

Things can go wrong when the people concerned are not involved in design decisions. The next part of this Case Study shows how involving the local people resulted in a successful housing development.

Research
Draw a floor plan of your home. How would you change it if you had the opportunity? Draw a plan of your ideal home. Write down any problems you might face when changing the shape of a house. What rules stop people doing what they like with their houses? If you can, ask a builder.

Getting it right

▲ *Houses in the town of Alto Mayo after the 1990 earthquake.*

On 29 May 1990 an earthquake caused widespread damage in the area of San Martin in Peru. Many of the local houses were made using the 'tapial' or 'rammed earth' method. The walls of such houses can be up to one metre thick and have no flexibility to withstand tremors. These houses were badly damaged by the earthquake.

1 What do you understand by the word 'flexible'? Look it up in a dictionary. Do you find the definition useful?

2 Make a list of materials you use that are flexible and those that are not.

▲ *The local people discussing the design and layout of their new houses.*

The tapial houses were built by people who had moved into the San Martin area from other places. This building technique was fine for houses in some areas of Peru, but not for those in an earthquake area.

A reconstruction programme designed and built new houses. Local people were involved in the design process and in making decisions about building materials and techniques. These houses were designed to suit the people who would live in them.

Pause for thought

How could you discuss design ideas with a large group of people? How would you make decisions if different groups of people disagreed?

Quincha – a traditional building technique

The new homes were built using a technique based on a traditional local building method called 'quincha'. Reeds and small branches are woven into a latticework pattern. This is supported between spaced horizontal and vertical poles, and a small amount of earth is used to fill the gaps.

When a second earthquake struck, on 4 April 1991, seventy houses and a large community building made by the quincha method were either completed or under construction. They all remained standing although there was widespread damage and loss of life in the area.

The adapted 'quincha' technique used for the new houses in Alto Mayo. ▶

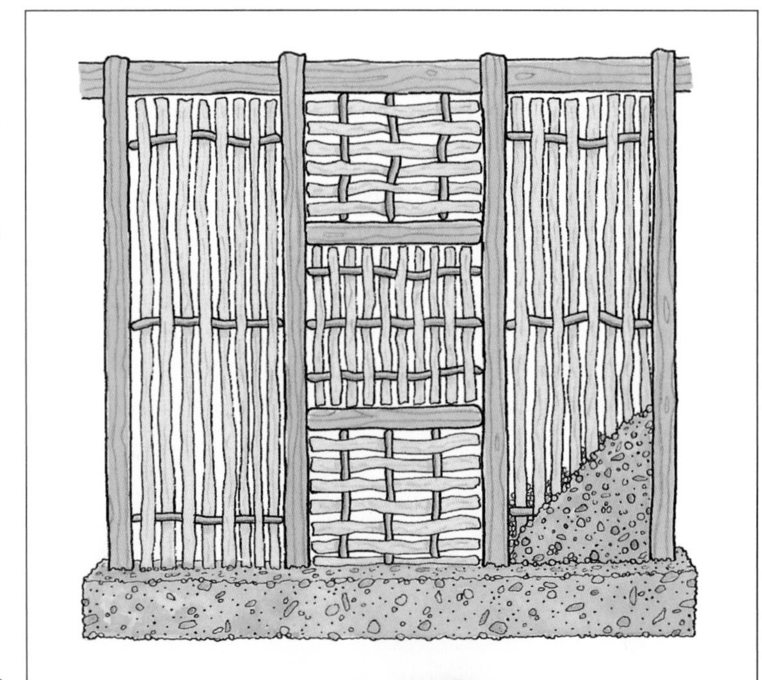

▲ *This house, built using the quincha technique, was still standing after the 1991 earthquake.*

The house designers had made use of local knowledge, so the houses they built were affordable, easily repaired and met the community's housing needs.

Next time you are designing ask yourself 'Who am I designing this for?' and 'How can I involve them in the design process?'.

Research

Why do you think these houses were so successful? What other parts of the world are affected by earthquakes? Do the buildings and houses in these areas have any special features?

9 Space planning – the layout of a superstore

The layout of a new superstore is very important to its future success – this is the job of the space planners

We live, work and enjoy ourselves in a variety of **environments**. Some activities, such as sleeping, eating and design and technology lessons, usually take place indoors. Others, such as sports, usually take place outdoors. Each of these environments must be designed to suit their purpose in the best possible way. Designing the layout of an indoor environment is called **space planning**. This Case Study describes how space planners design the layout of a large superstore.

▲ *Inside the superstore – the end result of the space planning work.*

Space planning is a little like putting together a huge jigsaw. Before we start, we need to know the amount of space available and the number of different pieces we need to fit in this space. Space planning for a superstore is extremely important. Mistakes in store layout might mean that the store loses customers or makes less money. Large supermarket chains such as Tesco have space planning departments to make sure that each of their stores is well laid out.

Identifying the pieces

A typical superstore might have a floor area of 4000 m^2. A large variety of goods is sold. Similar products are kept together in sales areas.

Pause for thought
How might a mistake in the store layout affect sales in the store?

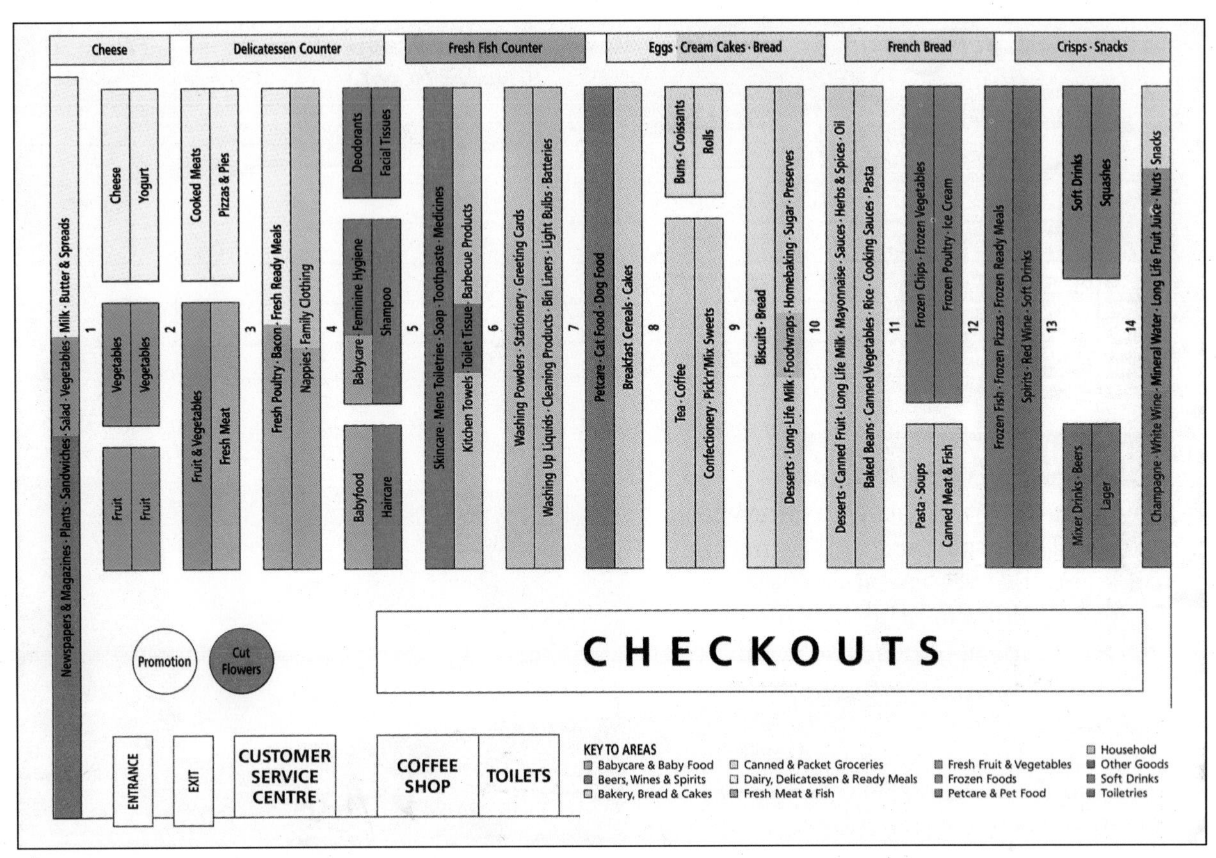

▲ *A floor plan of a typical superstore.*

A large superstore will have separate areas for:

- food, which may be fresh, packaged, frozen, bottled or canned;
- household goods such as detergent;
- beers, wines and spirits;
- health and beauty products such as shampoos and toothpaste.

There may be a bakery, a fresh fish counter, an area for dairy products, a meat counter and a delicatessen. Some superstores sell newspapers, magazines, books, sweets, toys and flowers and have a coffee shop. All superstores need space for check-outs.

The sizes of the pieces

How much space is given to each type of product will depend on the value of that product sold in a week. For example, a superstore might sell £500 000 of goods in a week, of which £55 000 is spent on frozen foods. Frozen foods therefore make up 11 per cent of the store's takings. So 11 per cent of the floor space will be given over to frozen foods.

1 Think about a superstore you have visited. List the different sales areas, such as the frozen food section.
2 List any special needs that each sales area might have. For example, the fresh fish department needs to be kept cool and well-ventilated.
3 Look back at your list of sales areas. Is there anything that you want to add to it? Can you think of any new requirements? For example, the beers, wines and spirits area will need to be closed off at times when it is illegal to sell alcoholic drinks.

1 The table shows the typical weekly takings for a superstore with 4000 m^2 of floor space. Work out each department's percentage of the total weekly sales.

2 How many square metres of the floor space should be given to the different departments? Frozen foods has been worked out for you.

Product department	*Weekly sales*	*Percentage of total weekly sales*	*Floor area*
Fruit and vegetables	£52 500		
Dairy produce	£52 500		
Frozen foods	£55 000	11 %	440 m^2
Meat	£27 500		
Groceries	£275 000		
Beers, wines and spirits	£37 500		
TOTAL	£500 000	100 %	4000 m^2

Planning constraints

Now that the space planners know the sizes of the jigsaw pieces, they need to think about how to arrange them. They must consider the customers as well as technical issues. The comfort of the customers and the impression that the store makes on them are important. How would you feel if the first things that you saw on entering the store were shelves full of disinfectant bottles? Technical issues include the need for electrical power and refrigeration. Each type of product needs special consideration.

Fresh food departments, such as the delicatessen, bakery and fish counters, need to be close to the storage areas at the back of the stores. Imagine the difficulties if fresh fish had to be carried a long distance through a busy store.

Frozen foods need to be kept in refrigerators close to the storage area so that the food does not defrost when it is being moved from the storage area to the sales area. But they also need to be close to the check-outs because customers tend to collect frozen foods at the end of their shopping.

▲ *The bakery.*

The frozen food section. ▶

Fruit and vegetables are placed at the front of the store near the entrance, because they are colourful, eye-catching and attract the customer.

Beers, wines and spirits need to be displayed close to the warehouse and close to the check-outs because they need constant supervision. The area may need to be closed off at times when it is illegal to sell alcoholic drinks.

▲ *The fruit and vegetable section.*

▲ *The alcoholic drinks section.*

Tinned goods are displayed close together. This makes stacking the shelves easier.

In each sales area the fastest selling products are placed on the lower shelves. Products that are similar, such as soft drinks, are displayed close together.

▲ *The tinned goods.*

Research

Visit your local superstore or supermarket. Make a sketch plan showing the floor area and the location of the different types of products. Estimate the amount of space given to each type of product.

We have seen how space planners design the layout of a superstore. The layout of a classroom, workshop, bedroom or dining area can all benefit from space planning.

Pause for thought

Try redesigning an indoor environment which you use.

10 Blue jeans and indigo dye

Natural indigo dye has been used for thousands of years but the popularity of blue jeans has led to the production of the modern synthetic dye in massive quantities

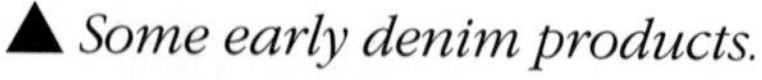
▲ *Some early denim products.*

Textiles in their natural state often look drab and boring. Dyes are used to colour them and make them more attractive and interesting.

Blue denim jeans were originally designed as tough, working clothes. These days they are also fashion items. There are jeans with designer labels and many people are loyal to one brand or style. None of this would have been possible without the indigo dye which is used to make denim.

Research

Find out how many people in your class own a pair of blue denim jeans. Do they own other items of clothing made from blue denim? Present your results as a graph.

Now look at people from different age-groups. You could group people into age bands – under 10, 10–19, 20–29 and so on. Try to talk to the same number of people in each age band. Produce a bar chart of your findings. Do denim jeans appeal to all age-groups or only some? You may be surprised by your results.

Natural indigo dye

Natural indigo was being used as a dye 4000 years before Levi Strauss produced his first pair of workman's jeans. There are traces of it in the linen wrappings of Egyptian mummies. It comes from the *Indigofera* plant which first grew in India. As people started travelling and trading, the plant spread from country to country. Today it is found in tropical climates throughout the world. By 1815 over one million people were altogether producing 3500 tonnes of natural indigo dye per year in India alone.

▲ *Mummy wrappings show traces of indigo.*

▲ *The indigo plant.*

Research

Many other natural dyes can be made. Beetroot and onion skins can both be used to dye textiles. Find out which other natural dyes can be made easily. Experiment with dyeing small scraps of material (be careful not to get any of the dye on your clothes). Write a report describing how you produced the dye. How even is the colour? What happens when you wash the material?

▲ *Wool coloured with natural dyes.*

Synthetic indigo takes over

In 1897 Adolf von Baeyer developed a formula for producing synthetic indigo dye after 12 years' research. The new synthetic indigo kept its colour and was easier to use than the traditional natural dye. The new dye quickly replaced the natural dye, and today most of the world's indigo dye is produced synthetically. The scale of production is massive. Each year 9000 tonnes of synthetic dye are produced, enough to dye many millions of pairs of jeans.

▲ *Adolf von Baeyer.*

1 Who gained and who lost by the development of the new synthetic dye? Produce a table of winners and losers saying how each group of people gained or lost.

Dyeing cotton

Indigo in its pure state does not dissolve in water. Before it can be used, the dye has to be treated to make it **soluble**. The cotton yarn is dipped 4–6 times in a vat containing the 'treated' indigo dye. After each dipping the dyed cotton is exposed to the air to turn the dye back into its original form.

Pause for thought
Why must the dye be changed back to its original form?

Producing denim

Denim is produced by criss-crossing indigo-dyed cotton thread with undyed, white cotton threads. One of the unique things about indigo is that it coats the surface of the cotton threads leaving them white on the inside. As the denim is worn the blue surface is rubbed off, exposing the white core. This gives denim its fashionable worn look. Today processes such as stone-washing are used to make new denim look worn.

Pause for thought
Why do people like their denim jeans to look as if they have been worn for a long time?

▲ *A close-up look at Denim*

New developments with indigo

The chemicals company ICI has developed a new technique for dyeing with indigo. The dye is contained in small, round, dry bubbles called **microperles**. Unlike dry powders or solid lumps they flow freely without sticking, produce no dangerous dust, and are easy to handle. These microperles burst on contact with water, releasing the dye which quickly spreads throughout the vat.

▲ *Microperles.*

▲ *Cotton dyed with indigo.*

What next?

Every technological development has consequences. People are more and more concerned with the environment. Dyeing many millions of pairs of jeans each year uses a lot of dye and water. Manufacturers have to find ways of disposing of the waste water which will not damage the environment.

Fashions in jeans change, with new colours or even white jeans becoming all the rage for a while. However, blue jeans seem to remain the most popular. People will probably be wearing jeans dyed with indigo for many more years.

▲ *Manufacturing denim jeans.*

1 Think about the production of blue jeans. How could the production of jeans be made more environmentally friendly? Write down a few of your ideas.

Written with the help of INTERMEDIATE TECHNOLOGY

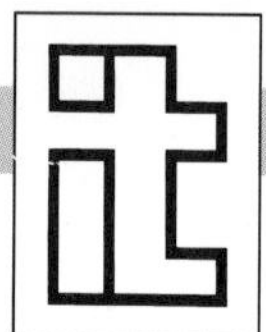

11 Fishing boats in South India – an appropriate technology?

Designing new boats to meet the changing needs of local fishermen meant developing new technology – but was it appropriate?

Kerala is a state in southern India with 590 km of coastline. There are 220 fishing villages with 130 000 fishermen who catch mackerel, sardines, shrimps and prawns, to eat and for local markets. About one million people in the area depend on fishing for their livelihoods. Fishing boats are shared by three or four families.

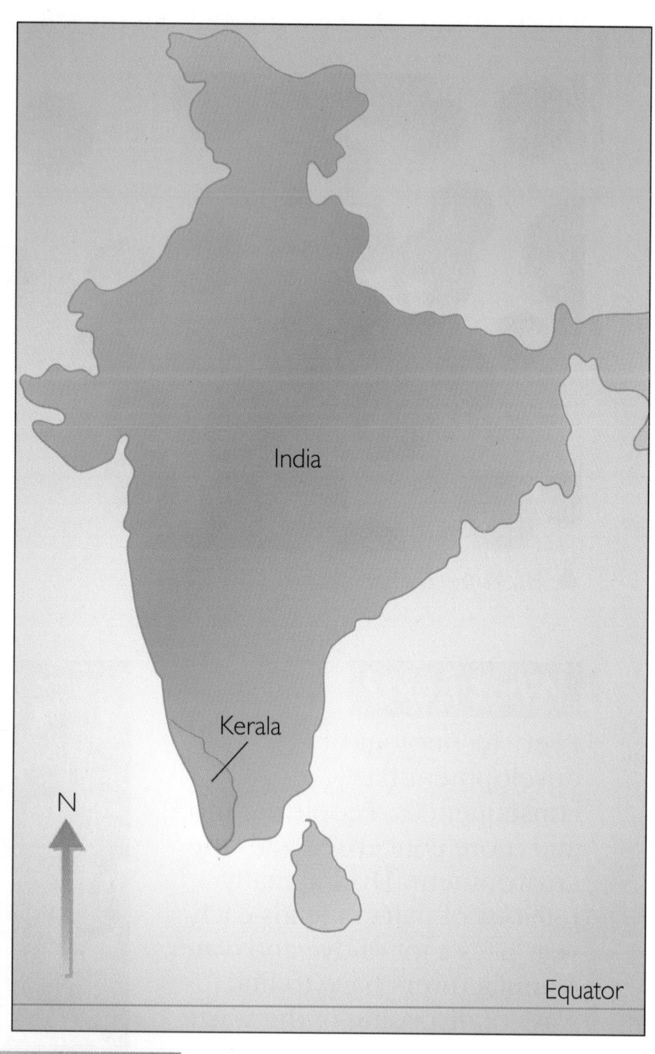

The traditional technologies

The traditional fishing boats were designed by the fishermen to meet their particular needs. Different types of boats are needed for different beaches and fishing techniques. In the south of Kerala the beaches are narrow and rocky with a lot of surf.

Pause for thought

What would someone designing a fishing boat for use in the south of Kerala need to think about?

▲ *A beach in South Kerala and the traditional kattumaram.*

The local people have developed a boat called a **kattumaram**. It is a raft made by tying together logs cut from local trees. It is unsinkable because the logs float. It is light and easily launched from beaches with heavy surf. Kattumarams can carry a large load. They last 6–10 years, and use either wind power or oars. Both are renewable energy sources.

Further north along the Kerala coast the beaches are wider but there is still a lot of surf. Here, the local fishermen have designed and made dug-out canoes called **vallams**. These boats are larger than kattumarams and can hold more fish. They are 8 metres long with parallel sides about 0.5 metres wide. They are stable and easy to handle. The fishermen use the off-shore breezes to sail out to their fishing grounds in the morning and the on-shore breezes to return home at night.

▲ *A North Kerala beach.*

Is it appropriate?

Both fishing boats are examples of **appropriate technologies**. They meet the needs of the people who use them.

1 Look at the criteria for appropriate technology in your *Student's Book*. Do you want to add anything? From what you have read so far, write down which criteria apply to the fishing boats in each case.

2 Are kattumarams and vallams examples of appropriate technologies?

▲ *The vallam favoured by the northern fishermen.*

A problem arises

The woods traditionally used for the kattumarams and the vallams are now very scarce and very expensive. The trees have been cut down for timber, construction and other domestic uses. Another available wood lasts only a year in sea water. Are the traditional ways of building boats still appropriate? Clearly new ways of building boats are needed.

Using new technologies

The fishermen's society in India asked for help in developing a new technology to produce replacement boats. A development charity and an English boat designer responded by introducing a new system for making boats called 'stitch-and-glue'. This is a simple technique using marine plywood and fibreglass which is used by DIY boatbuilders in Europe.

The plywood came from Indian hardwoods. Instead of hollowing out a trunk to make one boat, plywood from one tree could be used to make several boats. In 1980 this was a very economic material for boat building, and was available from Indian industries. The plywood was very strong and light. It could be used in many ways so boat design was not limited by the shape of wooden planks or solid trunks.

Resins and glassfibre were used to stitch and glue the boats together. These materials are made in India using fossil fuels.

▲ *The new stitch-and-glue method used for building boats with plywood.*

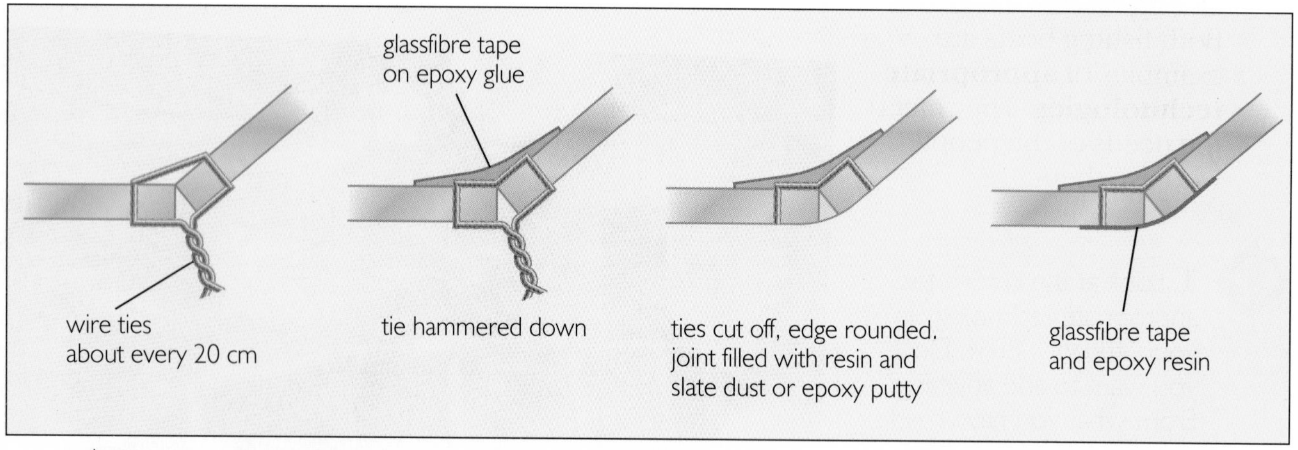

▲ *How stitch-and-glue works.*

Instead of copying the existing designs for vallams and kattumarams, the designers introduced a new design of boat to Kerala. A catamaran with two hulls was designed in England and tested in Sri Lanka. The designers had created a large, stable fishing platform which could be used further out to sea.

The new boat was made using what was in some ways an appropriate technology, but it had been designed without any help from the fishermen who would use it. They were unfamiliar with the new design and were not convinced it would suit their beaches. The new boat was much larger, difficult to launch and more expensive, even though it could carry a bigger load.

1 How would you score this boat against the appropriate technology criteria? Write down which criteria it meets.

▲ *A gilletkat, the new stitch-and-glue kattumaram.*

A local design

In the end the local fishermen proposed their own designs, based on their kattumarams but using the new stitch-and-glue technology. These new boats, called **gilletkats**, became very popular. The vallam fishermen and the boatbuilders in the North also proposed new designs based on traditional vallams, using the stitch-and-glue technique.

The two new types of boats are now being built in four locally owned boat-yards in Kerala. These boat-yards employ 100 people and build 200–250 boats a year. Recently, however, marine plywood has become expensive and scarce. Perhaps the people of Kerala will need to change their designs again.

2 Of all the boat designs described, which is the most appropriate and which the least?

Pause for thought
What lessons should we bear in mind when new technology is being developed to solve a problem?

▲ *A stitch-and-glue version of the vallam alongside a traditional vallam.*

12 Fire brigade command and control

An efficient communications system is vital for the fire service and it is the designers' and engineers' job to get it right

Firefighters often have to deal with complex accidents where there is great risk to themselves and members of the public. Their success depends on an excellent **communications system**. This Case Study looks at the communications system of a county fire brigade and how the different parts of the system fit together. This will help you to design communications systems of your own.

The accident

A lorry crashes into a motorway bridge late at night. This is how the incident develops.

2.43 a.m.
Silworth's two fire engines and their crews leave Silworth fire station. Fire brigade command and control contacts the fire station in Barchester, the nearest large town. It is told to send a fire engine to Silworth fire station as it is now empty, and a rescue tender to the scene of the accident.

2.46 a.m.
The two fire engines from Silworth and an ambulance arrive at the scene of the accident. Because of the risk of fire from the lorry's cargo, the station officer takes charge.

2.47 a.m.
Silworth station officer radios fire brigade command and control. The lorry bears the warning label 3YE, which means it may release dangerous fumes. People in the nearby houses will need to be moved away from the accident.

2.48 a.m.
Fire brigade command and control contacts Silworth police, telling them to organize an evacuation of the area.

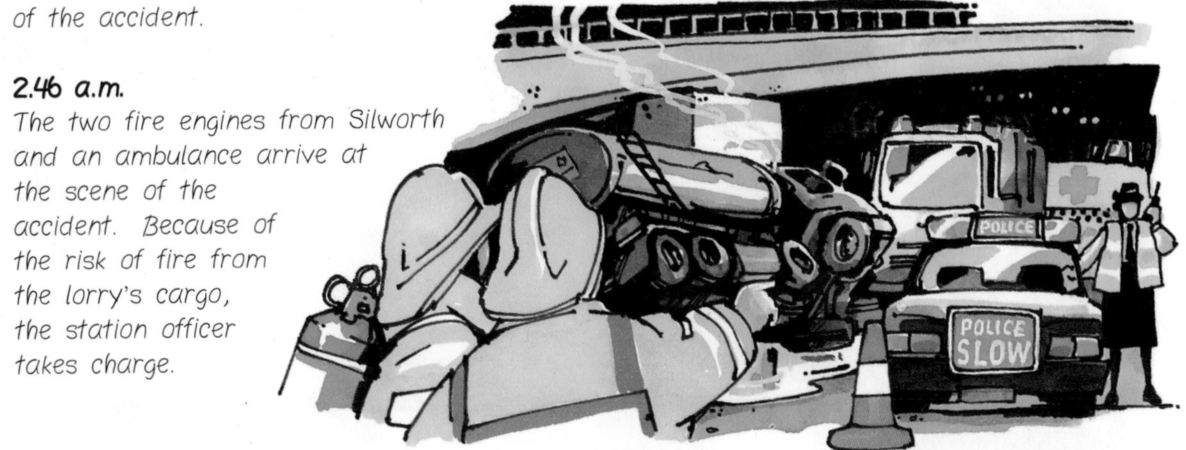

Less than twenty minutes have passed and things are getting complicated.

1 List all the different groups of people involved in dealing with the accident.

2 Which groups need to communicate with each other?

3 Draw a web diagram like the one opposite, showing the people and the links between them.

4 Write down what would happen if some of these links were broken and the people could not talk to each other.

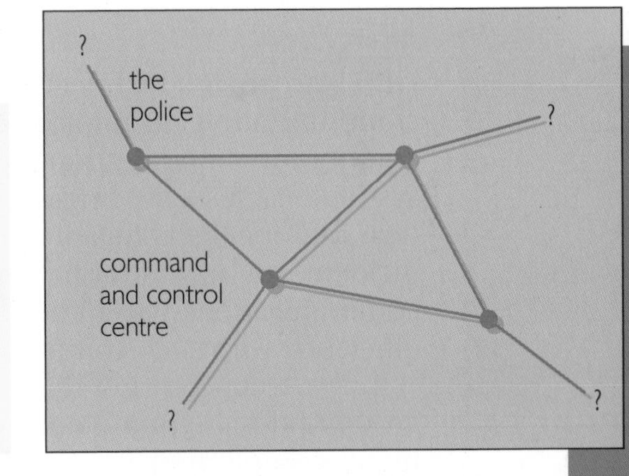

Organizing the system

All the most important communications in a fire brigade system pass through the control centre. The station officer does not telephone the police directly. The officer radios the command and control centre which then contacts the police. The people in contact with the centre pass on information to their teams.

5 What advantages can you see in this way of organizing a communications system? Make a list.

6 Draw a diagram showing how your school communicates with parents.

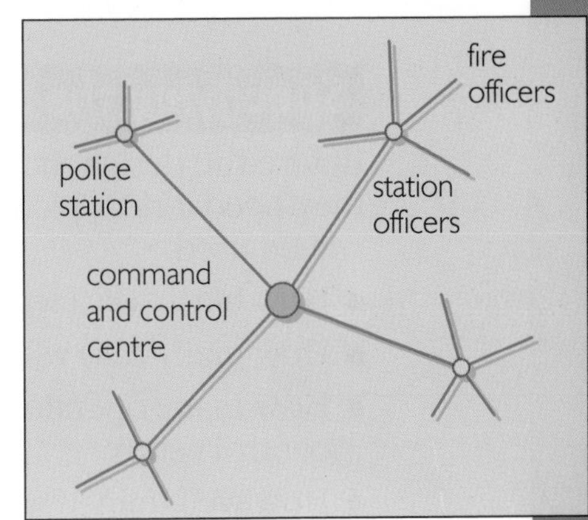

Marconi MACE – a real command and control system

▲ *The command and control centre of the London Fire Brigade.*

GEC Marconi is a high technology micro-electronics and communications technology company. It has developed a computer communications system called Marconi MACE. The system enables a fire brigade command and control centre to deal with incidents reliably and efficiently. Even the simplest incident can become complicated. To be useful, a communications system needs to be able to cope quickly and efficiently with such complications.

In the second part of this Case Study we look at how a group of designers and engineers design and produce such a highly complicated and sophisticated system.

Pause for thought
Imagine you are designing a communications system for your school. With whom would you need to talk to help you produce a specification? What questions would you ask them?

Specifying the system

Before the designers and engineers can produce the system they need a clear picture of what it will have to do and how it will be used.

- How big an area will it need to cover?
- How many calls will it have to deal with?
- How many operators will there be at the command and control centre?
- How well trained will the operators be?
- Will back-up systems be needed in case of power failure?

1 Write a specification for a communications system for your school, listing all the things it would need to do and how it would be used.

The design engineers find out the answers to these, and many more, questions by listening to the client – in this case the fire brigade officers.

When the design engineers have gathered all the information they need, and understand how the system will be used and what it will have to do, they write a **system specification**. This document will be agreed with the client so that everyone knows exactly what system is going to be produced.

▲ *An old-style command and control system.*

Unexpected benefits

In the past, *manual* command and control systems were used. The fire stations where all the appliances were based were held on cards which were filed. The current situation was recorded on a board.

Modern computerized systems, as well as meeting all the requirements for a command and control centre, have been found to have unexpected benefits.

- Low priority calls, where there is no risk of fire spreading, are grouped together by the computer so that one fire vehicle can make several calls without returning to the fire station.
- All information is recorded automatically so that the fire brigade can check the use of all its appliances and make sure it is responding quickly and efficiently to calls.
- All communications are recorded automatically in case of legal action over arson, wrong information or hoax calls.

Pause for thought

If the school communications system you wrote a specification for was computer-based, what additional benefits might this bring?

13 Keeping it clean – the automatic washing machine

An automatic washing machine is a system with inputs, outputs and controls, designed to cope with a wide range of needs

Sweaters, shirts, jeans, T-shirts, sheets and towels all need regular cleaning. For most of us that means putting them in the washing machine. There are alternatives of course. Some delicate fabrics are still best washed by hand. In many parts of the world, washing clothes is a social activity, a chance to talk to neighbours and catch up with the local news. This Case Study looks at the automatic washing machine as a system, with **inputs, outputs** and **controls**. We see how engineers and designers at companies such as GEC Hotpoint design a washing machine which can cope with all sorts of fabrics.

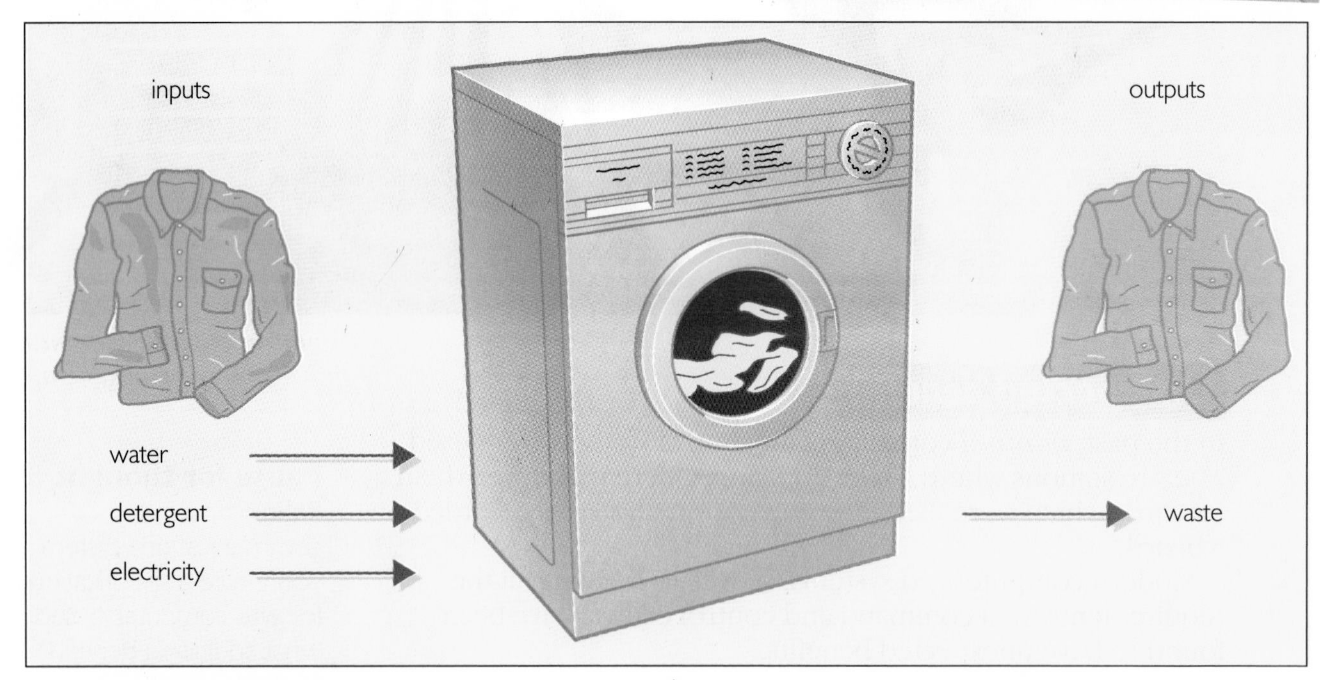

▲ *The inputs to and outputs from an automatic washing machine.*

Inputs and outputs

The picture shows a washing machine with its inputs and outputs. Whichever way we wash fabrics we need a good supply of water, detergent and energy to heat the water and move the fabrics around, as well as drainage for the dirty water. Water, and electricity for the heater and motor, are supplied to our homes. Detergent we can buy from the shops.

Pause for thought
Think of some other household appliances. What are their inputs and outputs?

Programming the sequence

Imagine how complicated it would be to design a washing machine if every item of clothing needed a slightly different washing cycle. Most clothes are labelled with a code which shows the temperature of the water and the amount of motion needed to clean the garment without damaging it. Clothing, washing machine and detergent manufacturers have agreed on a set of standard washing cycles for all automatic washing machines. This means that manufacturers can design a variety of machines which can all wash according to the codes on garment labels.

Pause for thought
Think of industries in which companies have agreed on a set of standards. VHS in the video industry is a good example.

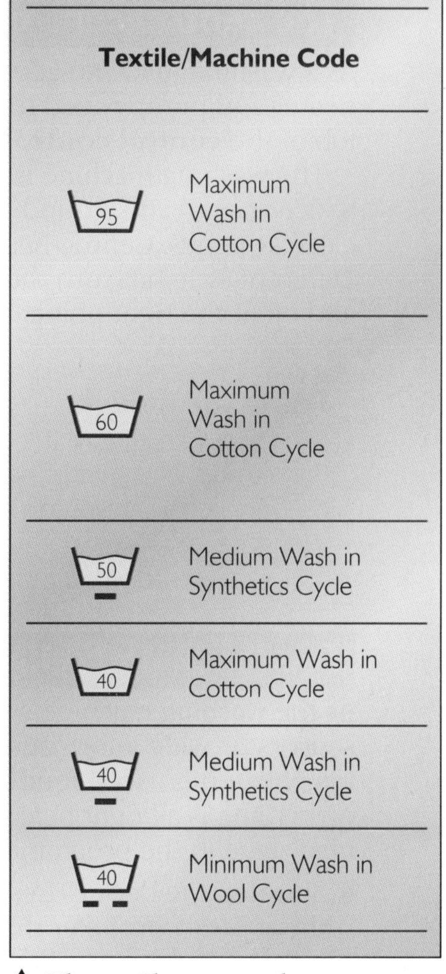

▲ *The textile care code.*

Controlling the cycle

```
 1  Check that the door is locked.
 2  Fill machine with water.
 3  Heat water to 50 °C.
 4  Turn on the motor for 20
    minutes.
 5  Stop the motor.
 6  Empty the water.
 7  Add clean water to rinse the
    clothes.
 8  Turn on the motor for 5
    minutes.
 9  Stop the motor.
10  Empty the water.
11  Release the door catch.
```

▲ *A programme for a washing cycle.*

The great advantage of the modern washing machine is that it does all the hard work for you. You just put your dirty clothes in the drum, add detergent, close the door and choose the washing programme. Then you switch the machine on and leave it to do the job. It does not need constant supervision. This is because the washing machine has a **control system** which checks that everything is all right as it follows the washing programme.

The washing programme is a set of instructions which the machine follows for each washing cycle. Opposite is an example of a simple cycle for washing and rinsing clothes.

1 Look at the example of a simple washing cycle. What things does the machine need to check as it goes through the cycle?

2 Which steps in the cycle would need to change for different materials such as cotton, silk or wool?

The central controller

As a washing machine goes through its cycle the main motor, heater and pumps need to be turned on and off. This is the job of the **central controller**.

The washing machine is usually controlled by a timer motor which turns 'cams' round very slowly. These cams open and close switches. Central-heating timers work in the same way. Different switches turn the pump, heater and main motor on and off at the right points in the programme.

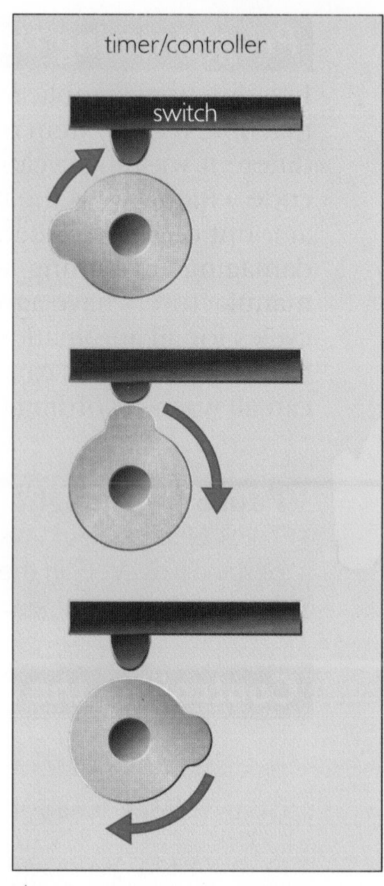

▲ *As the cam turns the switch opens and closes.*

Pause for thought
What would happen if the timer motor turned too quickly or too slowly? What would happen if the timer motor jammed in one position? Can you think of other ways of controlling a sequence?

Feedback and sensors

As the washing machine goes through its cycle, various sensors provide information to the central controller. This information is called **feedback**. This feedback shows that everything is all right before the controller moves on to the next stage in the programme.

- Shutting the door closes an 'interlock switch' which tells the central controller that the door is closed.

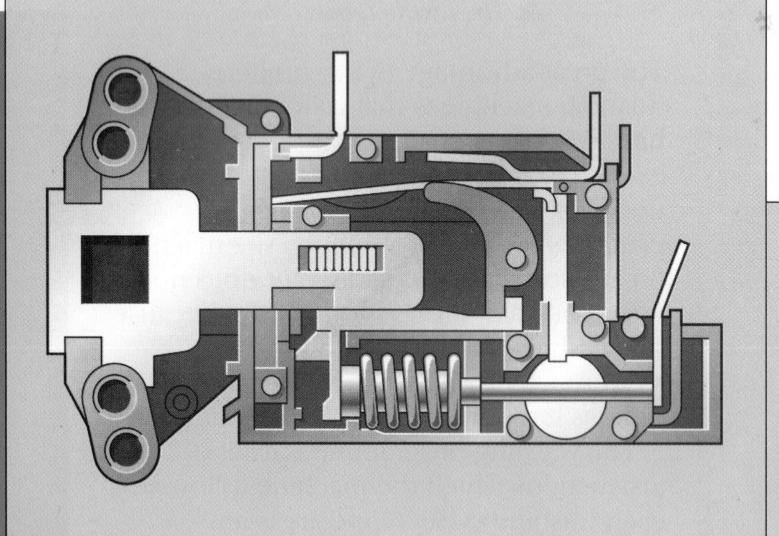

- As the drum fills up the water pushes air against a pressure switch. The pressure switch tells the central controller when there is enough water in the machine.

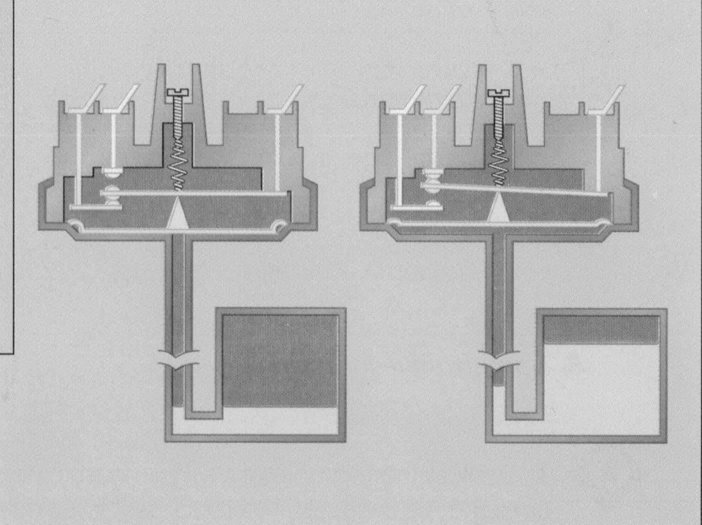

- A temperature sensor measures the temperature of the water. This temperature sensor is connected to the central controller which turns the heater on and off.

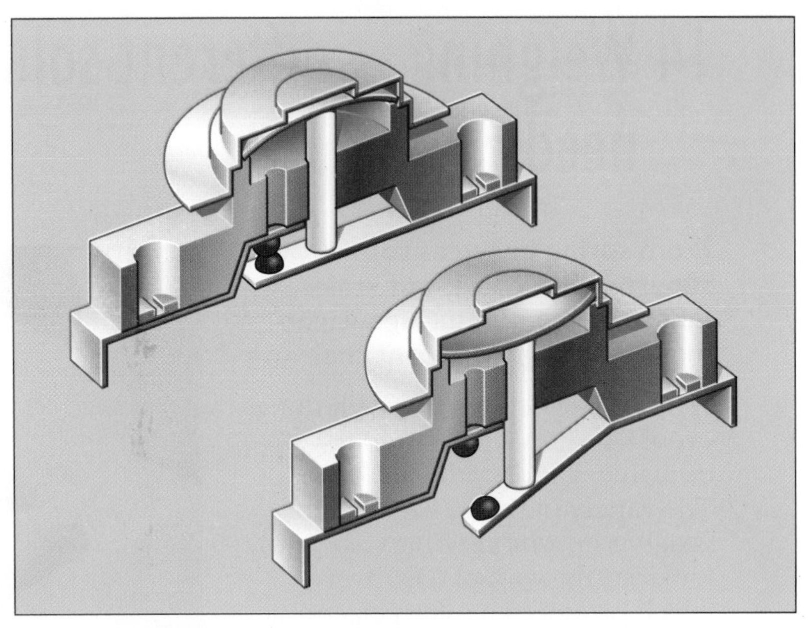

1 Think of other ways of checking the water level, temperature and door lock in a washing machine. Use sketches to show how these might work.

The complete system

An automatic washing machine follows a sequence of instructions every time it is used. Once a programme has been selected, the machine's central control system makes sure that the cycle is followed correctly. It can wash delicate fabrics or tough denim jeans equally successfully with very little help from us.

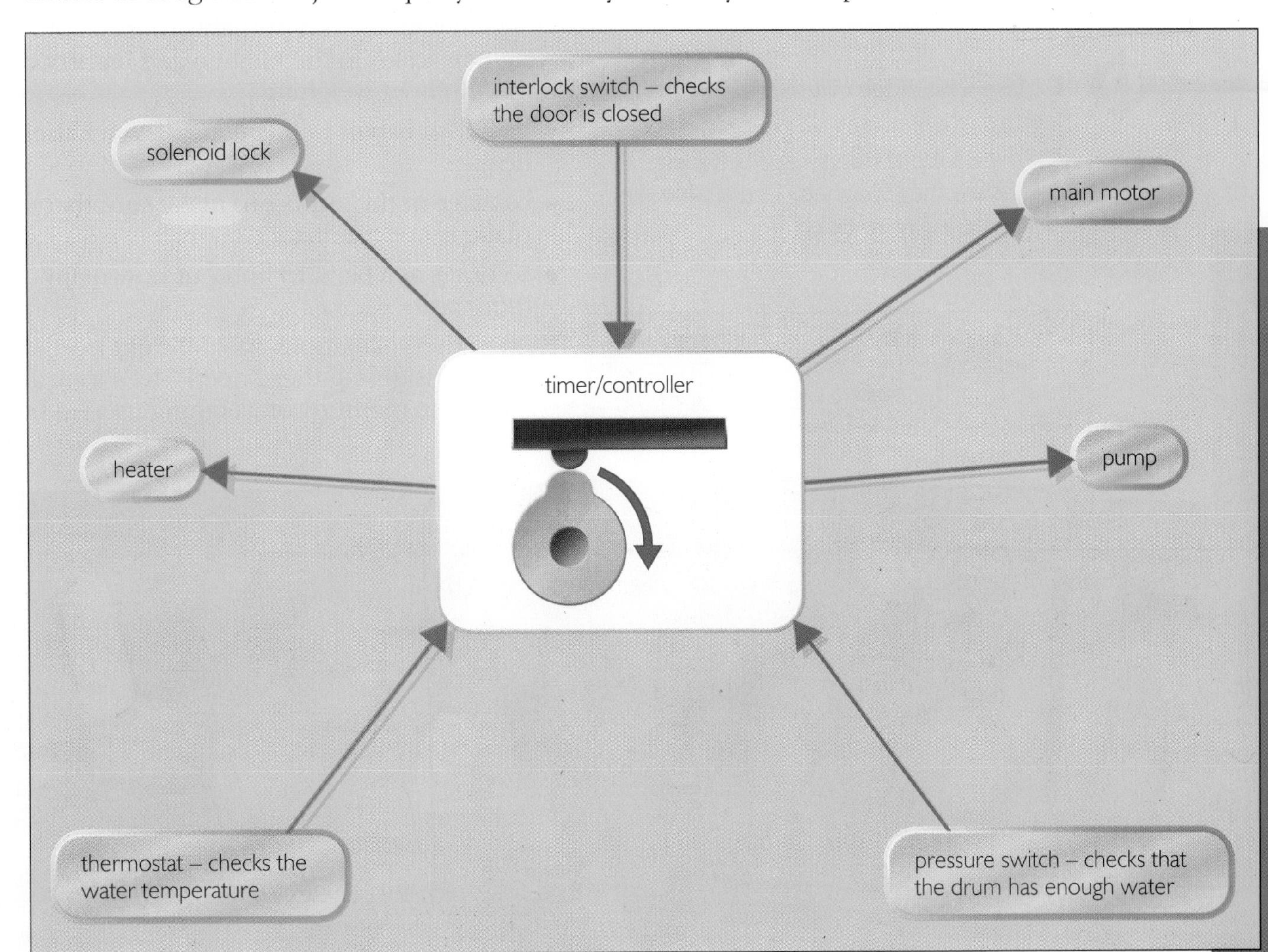

▲ *The complete system.*

14 Weighing – different solutions for different needs

From spring balances to supermarket check-out scales, machines for measuring weight must be designed to suit their use

People have needed to weigh things ever since they first started to exchange goods with each other. The variety of things we need to weigh is enormous. This Case Study looks at the work of GEC Avery, which produces modern electronic weighing machines. It will help you understand what needs to be considered when designing a weighing machine.

1 Make a list of ten different things that need weighing.

2 Why do these things need weighing? Where are they weighed? Use a table like this to record your ideas.

What?	Why?	Where?
flour	cooking	kitchen

How did you do? You probably thought of weighing scales in the kitchen and bathroom, but how about weighing:

- newborn babies in hospitals to check their health?
- baggage at the airport to make sure that the plane is not overloaded?
- £5 notes at a bank to find out how many there are?

Each of these situations has different needs. Before considering these needs, let's look at some of the methods of weighing used in the past.

Weighing – then and now

The 'time-line' across the bottom of pages 114–7 shows the history of weighing. Some of these ideas are thousands of years old, yet we still use them today. Others use the most recent developments in electronics. A spring balance is not as accurate as an electronic weighing machine, but it is cheap and portable and is still the most popular choice for anglers weighing their fish.

Q

3 Look at each of the weighing machines shown in the time-line. Write down advantages and disadvantages for each type.

4 Where might each of the weighing machines shown still be in use today?

The right choice

To design a weighing machine we need to think about:

- **Accuracy** – Drugs in a hospital may have to be weighed to the nearest thousandth of a gram. Vegetables can be weighed a lot less accurately.
- **Environment** – Is the machine being used indoors or outdoors? Is it in a clean or a dirty area? Is there a risk of dampness or overheating?
- **Range** – How much variation in weight is there in the things we are weighing?
- **Portability** – Does the machine need to be moved from place to place?
- **Reliability** – A spring could become overstretched, either by being tampered with or by overloading.
- **Ease of use** – Would we have to train someone to use the machine?
- **Servicing** – Is it easy to repair?
- **Running costs** – For example a portable electronic balance would need batteries.

5 Look back at your table. For each situation write down the most important factors an engineer needs to think about when designing a weighing machine.

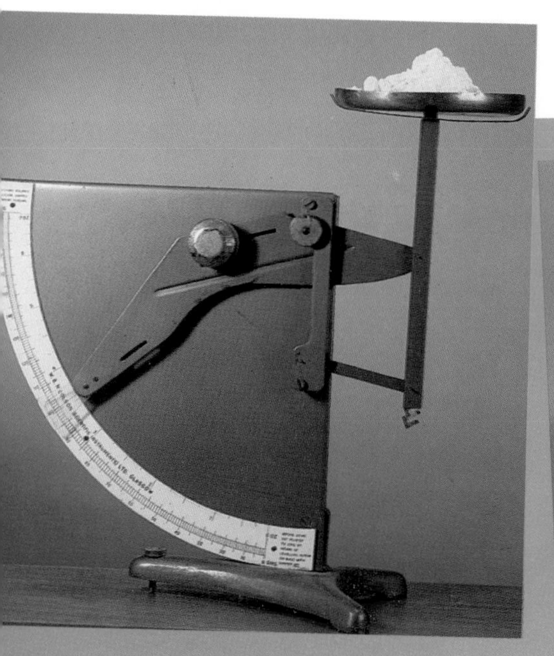

▲ *The development of the weighing machine.*

Weighing machines

At the heart of each of the scales in the time-line is a component which responds to weight. It might be a spring which stretches, a lever arm which tips, or a piece of material which twists or stretches. Can you think of other possibilities?

1 Look at the designs for weighing machines in the picture opposite. Choose one and make it.

2 Calibrate a scale for the weighing machine using 1p coins as weights. Use your machine to weigh some small objects.

3 Evaluate your weighing machine. Describe how you made it, how easy it was to use and any improvements you could make.

▲ *A load cell from an electronic weighing machine.*

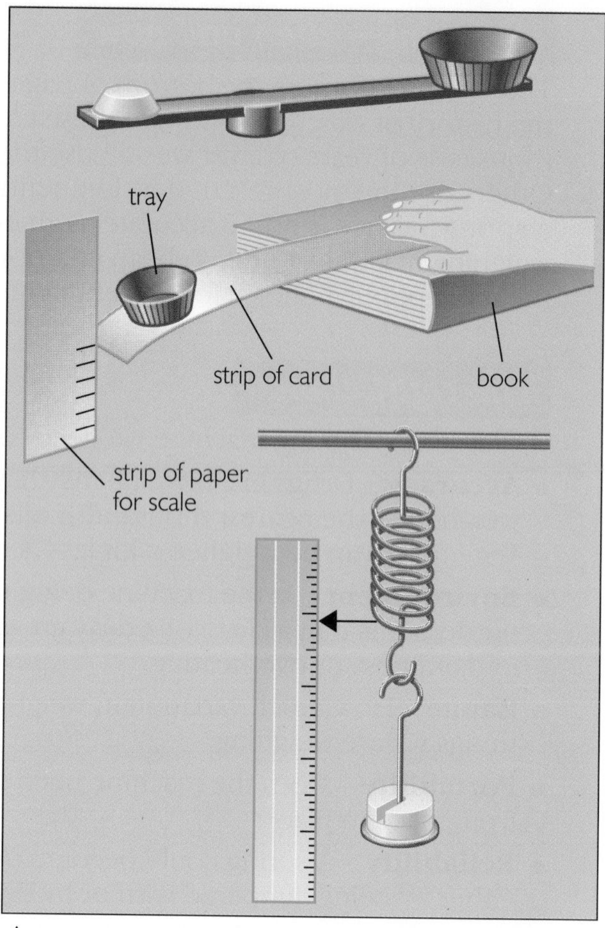

▲ *Simple weighing machines you can make.*

Electronic weighing machines

The heart of a modern electronic weighing machine is a **load cell**. This produces an electrical signal when it is squashed. The signal is processed by an electronic circuit which controls a display.

Electrical signals can be carried along wires, so the object being weighed and the display can be some distance apart, even in different rooms. The signal can even be sent to another electronic device such as an alarm system, printer or computer.

Pause for thought
Why might it be useful to separate the object being weighed and the display? The electronic weighing machine can easily be used as part of a larger system in a factory, supermarket or airport check-in.

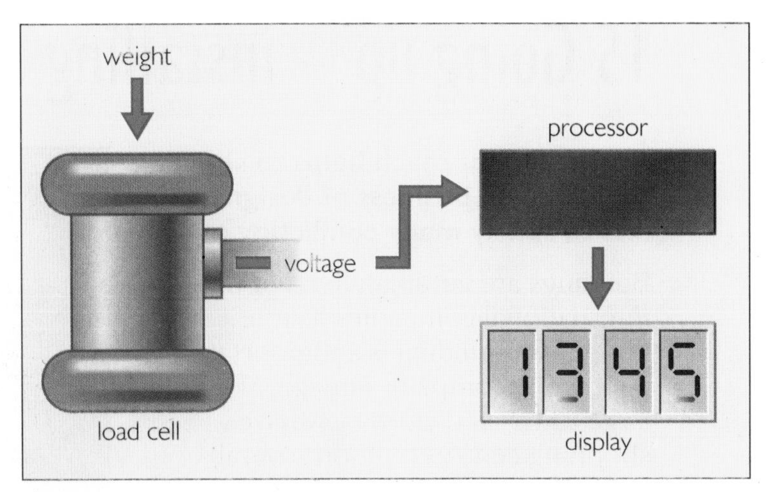

▲ *The components of a modern electronic weighing machine.*

▲ *Buying groceries in Victorian times.*

Buying our groceries

There have been several developments at supermarket check-outs. Tills are computerized. Barcode readers identify goods and give prices. Electronic weighing machines weigh and price vegetables. A complete list of all the stock in the store is held on a computer which can order new stock as things run out. But, however the check-out of the future develops, some things will always need weighing before they are sold.

4 The picture opposite shows a visit to a grocery shop one hundred years ago. How would it have differed from visiting a supermarket? List your ideas.

15 Going up – installing a lift

A systems approach helps to simplify the complex business of designing lifts to satisfy many conflicting needs

Buildings are getting taller. For many international companies a large impressive building is an important part of the company's image. Many large towns and cities now have shopping centres built on several levels, with additional levels for car parking. For these buildings to work properly people need to be able to move from floor to floor quickly and easily. An efficient 'vertical transport system' is essential for the smooth running of such buildings.

Pause for thought
An office block may be thirty storeys high. Estimate how long it would take you to walk up the stairs from the ground floor to the top.

▲ *The Nat West Tower in the City of London.*

Express Lifts Ltd has designed, made and installed lifts in some of the most famous buildings in London. For the Nat West Tower it produced special double-decker units. For the headquarters of Lloyds of London external 'wallclimbers' were supplied.

Different perspectives

Lift designers have to take various people's views into account. In a new office block, for instance, the architect will want the lift to fit in with the overall design of the building. The company will want the lift to be efficient, to give visitors a good impression and to be cheap to run. It may want to restrict use of the lift to staff and designated visitors for security reasons. Users will want to get to the floor they need without wasting time stopping at other floors or waiting. Some might want to travel as quickly as possible, despite the discomfort, while others might prefer a slower, smoother ride.

1 All the people involved will have different opinions about the lift. Write down how they might disagree and how these disagreements could be resolved.
2 List the most important factors to consider if you are designing an office lift system.

Different locations

Old people's homes, shopping centres and theme parks might also need efficient lift systems.

3 List five different places where a lift system might be needed. For each place list the factors that the lift designers would need to think about.

4 Which factors are common to each place? Which are different?

Planning and preparing

The installation of a lift is the final stage of months of work by engineers and designers. They try to meet the needs of all the different people involved. Designs are modified and models (**prototypes**) of the lift tested for efficiency, reliability and safety. In any project of this kind the designers and engineers have to balance many different needs.

Let's think about some of these needs.

- People want to travel quickly but faster lifts need more powerful motors which use more energy. Rapid acceleration can also be uncomfortable.
- Larger lifts carry more people but they need stronger, more expensive cables and more powerful motors.
- The more lifts in a building the less time people will have to wait, but too many lift shafts could weaken the building's structure.
- External lifts or 'wallclimbers' can make the journey more interesting but they are difficult to maintain.
- People need to be stopped from opening the doors between floors but must be able to escape if things go wrong, for instance if there is a power cut.

Designing a lift system is clearly very complicated. The next part of this Case Study shows how the engineers and designers go about it.

▲ *Balancing the constraints.*

A systems approach

It would be far too complicated to design a lift and think about all these needs at the same time. No one person could keep track of all the different factors. To simplify things lift designers use a **systems approach**.

The lift system is divided up into a set of **subsystems**. Each subsystem deals with one part of the design. For example, there might be a subsystem which opens and closes the doors. Another subsystem will call the lift.

Each subsystem might be designed separately although, of course, they all need to work together to make the lift operate. Each engineer and designer can work on one subsystem without needing to understand all the details of the other parts of the system.

Pause for thought
What other things might be designed using a systems approach?

The supersystem

There are times when what is happening to one lift may affect another. For example, someone on the second floor of a building calls for a lift to go up. There are two lifts in the building, one on the first floor going down and the other on the third floor going up. Which should answer the call? If the system is not designed properly both lifts might answer the same call. Modern lift systems have a **central controller** which links all the lifts together. It will check to see which lift is nearest to a call and make sure that all the lifts are used in the most efficient way. This central controller is part of the **supersystem**.

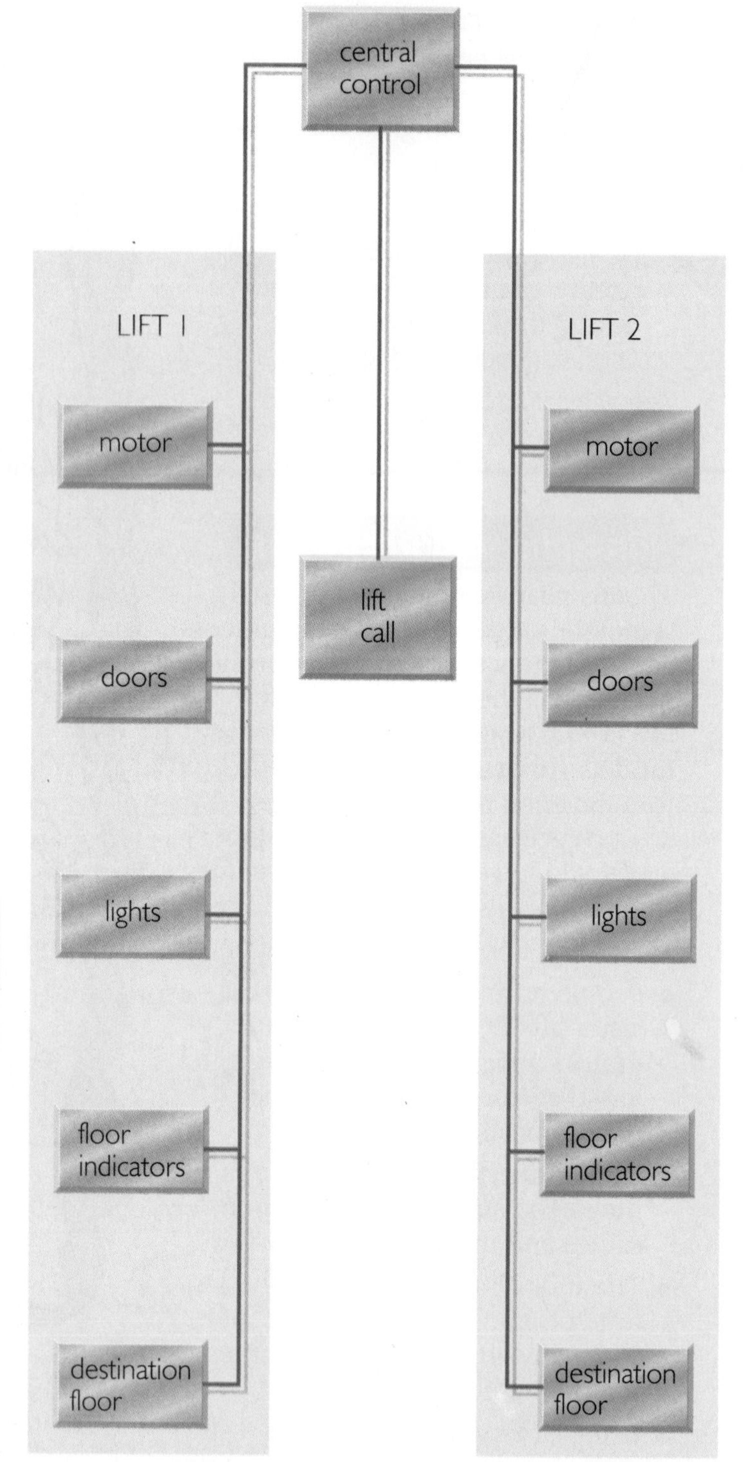

▲ *Systems, subsystems and the supersystem.*

1 List all the different subsystems needed for each lift in a lift system.

2 Which needs to be controlled by the supersystem's central controller?

3 Which would be controlled separately by each lift?

Testing the subsystems

The engineers who design each subsystem have to solve problems and make decisions. The engineers at Express Lifts Ltd spend a lot of time testing each subsystem before they are put together to make a complete lift. There is a huge test tower where different motors can be tested to see how much energy they use. Different speeds and accelerations can be tried to see which would produce the quickest, smoothest ride.

Next time you use a lift think about the time and care that has been taken to make sure that your journey is as quick and comfortable as possible.

Express Lifts' test tower at Northampton. ▶

16 Designing for safety

A small company designs a safety barrier to make football matches safer for spectators

All over the world thousands of people crowd together in stadiums to support their local teams, watch athletics events or listen to concerts. Often people are standing, trying to get the best view. Accidents are rare in these large crowds, but when they happen the results can be tragic. People can be pushed by the weight of the crowd, and end up trapped against the fences which divide the different sections of the stadium.

Ways of improving safety in large stadiums need careful thought. If the crowds at football matches were seated this would be safer but many spectators prefer to stand. If all the fences were removed this might stop people being crushed against them, but would it make the stadium safer?

1 There are many ways in which safety could be improved in large stadiums. Make a list of some of the important ones.

2 Which of these would be easy to introduce?

3 Which might spoil people's enjoyment of the event?

4 Which might be difficult to introduce?

Pause for thought
Why do you think some people might prefer to stand at football matches?

Following a recent tragedy at a football ground in England, designers at Soltrepac Ltd decided to try to develop a safer type of fence. If the pressure of people pushing against it rose above a certain limit this fence should collapse before anyone was crushed.

▲ *Being in a crowd is part of the excitement, but it can be dangerous.*

A specification for the fence

Before making the fence the designers thought about all the different problems they would need to solve.

Pause for thought

If you were designing this fence what things would you need to think about?

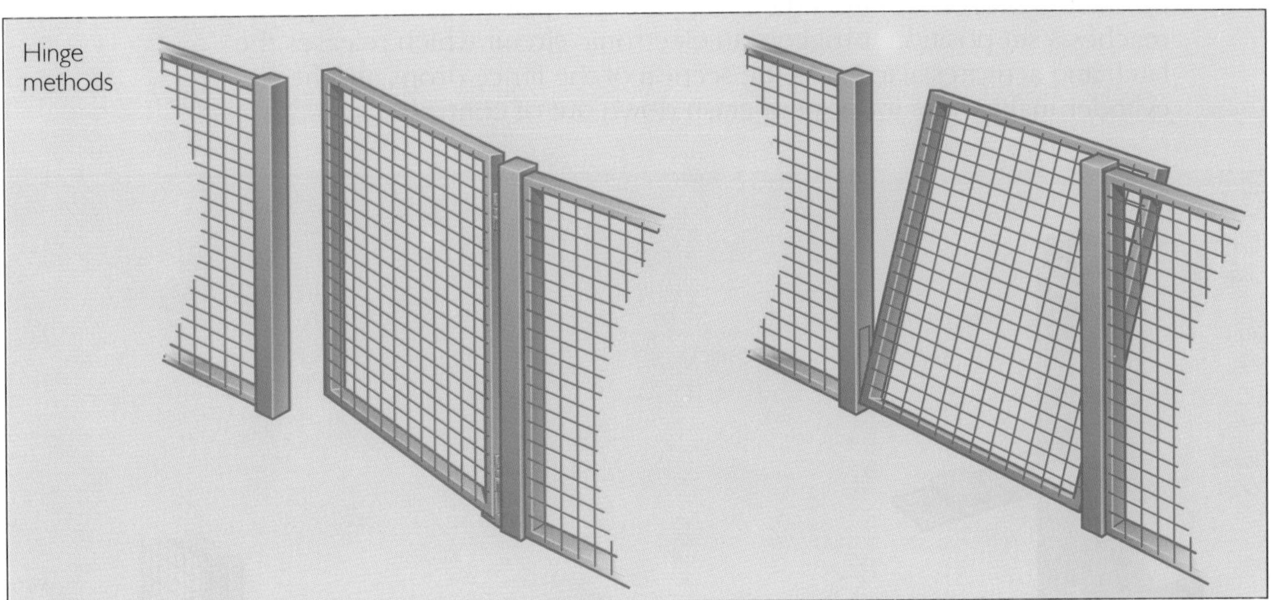

The fence designers agreed on these important points:

- The fence needs to collapse without breaking so that it does not have to be replaced every time it is used.
- The fence must not collapse suddenly or people would fall over and be trampled by the crowd behind them.
- The fence must not collapse if a few trouble-makers try to push it down.
- The fence needs to be adjustable.
- The fence needs a manual control as well as an automatic one.

Designing the fencing

After careful research the designers came up with ideas for the main parts of the system:

- The fence is made up of sections supported by fixed posts.
- Each section can either fold down or swing open like a gate.
- Each section is held in place by a latch which is released when the crowd pressure builds up.
- A damper cylinder stops the fence sections swinging open too quickly.

How do these different parts work together in the complete system design?

The first design

In the first design the fence sections collapse by folding flat to the ground. Each section pivots on two pins and is held in place by a latch. As the pressure on the fence builds up it pushes against a piston in a cylinder. A sensor monitors the position of the piston. When the piston reaches a set position it triggers an electronic circuit which releases the latch and activates alarms. As the section of the fence drops another cylinder makes sure it does not crash down out of control.

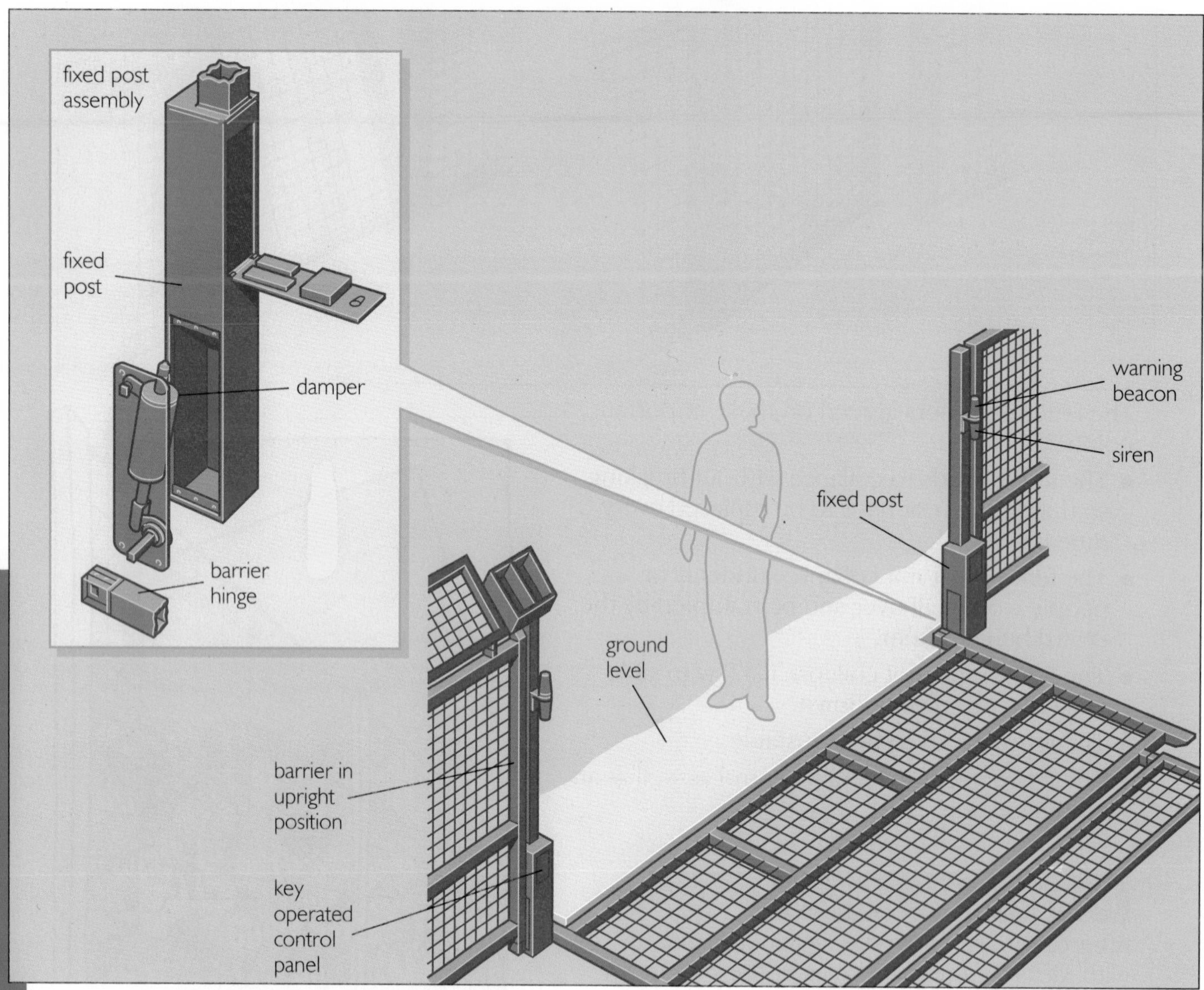

▲ *The first design, with fence sections that collapse to the ground.*

A time delay is built in so that the system only reacts to continued pressure, not to sudden attacks by vandals. The fence is supported by posts which are fixed firmly in the ground. These posts can be installed quite cheaply. All the wires and tubing are hidden inside the posts so that they cannot be tampered with. The fence sections can also be made to collapse in an emergency by using a key.

Pause for thought

Think about the first design for the fence. Have the designers thought about all the important factors? Which parts of this design do you like? Can you see any problems with it?

Modifying the design

The first fence was designed so that the sections fold down flat to the ground rather than swing open like gates. The designers chose this method because a gate design does not respond equally to pressure at all points. Try closing a door by pushing close to the hinge and then by pushing as far from the hinge as possible. It is a lot harder to move the door when you are pushing close to the hinge.

The designers were worried that if they used a swinging gate design for the fence, a spectator being crushed close to the hinge might not trigger the system. However, there were more serious problems with the folding flat design. Spectators close to the fence could be pushed over by the crowd behind as the fence fell to the ground.

The designers decided, on balance, to go for the swinging gate design. They had to redesign the system so that it was just as sensitive to pressure close to the hinge as it was to pressure at the far edge. This was done by redesigning the hinge mechanism.

▲ *Where you push makes a difference.*

▲ *The final swinging gate design.*

The final design

The picture on the left shows the final design for the safety fence.

1 Think of the rooms you work in at school. List any improvements which would make these areas safer.

2 Which of these improvements could be made by designing or redesigning something?

Written with the help of INTERMEDIATE TECHNOLOGY

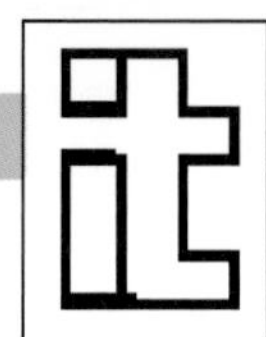

17 The salt of the earth – new technology in Sierra Leone

Women in Sierra Leone have developed new technologies and skills to extract high quality salt from silt

All over the world salt is used for adding taste and for preserving food. For many people it is a valuable item of trade. References to salt appear throughout history – the word 'salary' comes from the Latin for salt. In 1930 the Indian leader, Gandhi, led a march to the sea to protest about the British salt tax on Indians. His action was taken up by villagers collecting salt all along the coast. This action challenged British rule in India.

▲ *Salt produced by women in Sierra Leone.*

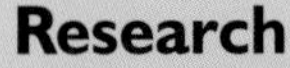

Research
Find out about the history of salt in Britain. Where was it produced? How was it used to preserve food?

In Sierra Leone, in West Africa, a lot of the salt used is imported from other countries, but about 35 per cent is produced locally. Most of the work is done by women.

The traditional way of producing salt in Sierra Leone was to boil sea water in earthenware pots over open fires. As the water evaporated the salt crystallized and was removed. This wet salt was then dried in the sun. The salt produced was of poor quality and much valuable wood was used for boiling the water.

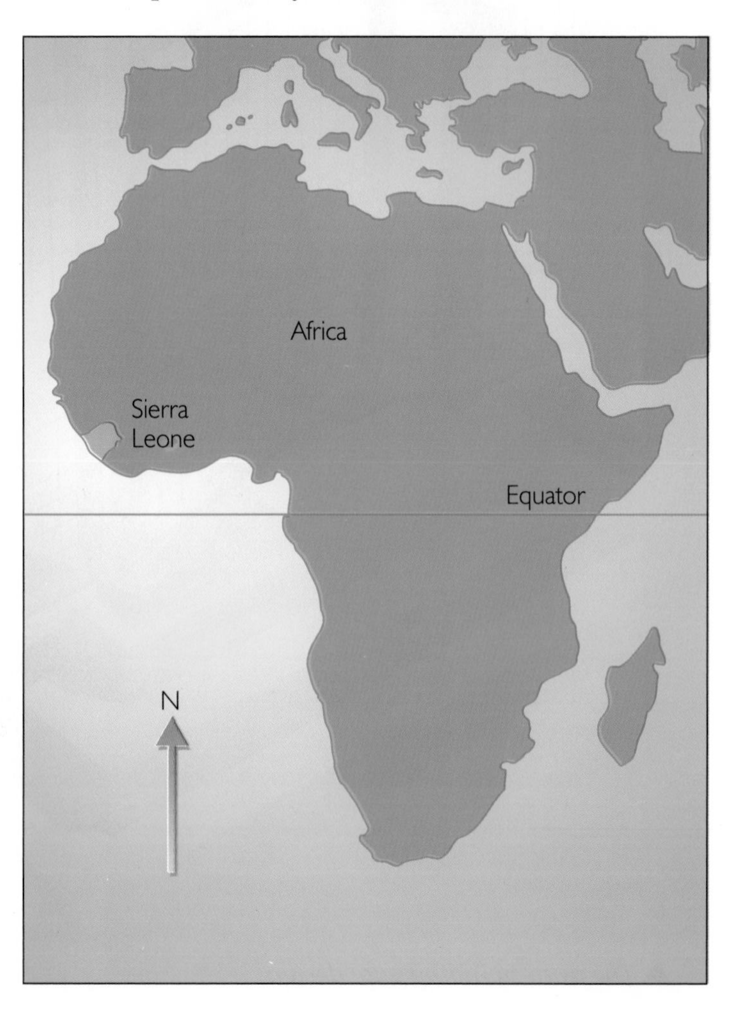

Research
Sierra Leone has a very interesting history. Find out about the country and its people. How do the people meet their needs for food, housing and shelter?

The women hit on the idea of digging ponds which filled up with sea water at high tide. Between high and low tide the sun evaporated some of the water, increasing the strength of the remaining salty water or *brine*. At low tide this concentrated brine was collected and boiled until salt crystals formed.

Pause for thought
How would you extract salt from sea water?

Salt from silt

The women then developed a technique to extract salt from the silt which collects where rivers join the sea. This silt is a mixture of sand, solid salt and water containing dissolved chemicals, including more salt.

Pause for thought
The first step is to remove the sand from the mixture. How would you do this ?

▲ *The traditional wooden baskets used by soap makers.*

The new technique

To extract the salt from the silt the women adapted the perforated baskets traditionally used by women soap makers. The salty silt is collected from the creek bottoms. It is then mixed with sea water which dissolves any solid salt. The mixture is left to settle in the baskets, which have plaster linings so that they act as filter funnels. The salty water runs through into wooden troughs below, leaving the sandy silt behind.

Finally, the women boil the salty liquid on a fire. Extra stones are put round the fire for protection so that it uses less fuel.

▲ *The lined wooden baskets filled with silt and sea water. In the background you can see silt ready for processing.*

1 How does the method of extracting salt from silt used by women in Sierra Leone compare with the way you do it in your school science lab? Draw labelled diagrams of the different steps you would use.

2 Why is it important that the salt production does not use much fuel?

▲ *Separating sand from salt water in the school science lab.* ▶

Improvements

The women experimented with the shape of their filter funnel. Now they use a rectangular design. This makes the process faster and more efficient.

The dishes in which the brine is boiled have also been improved. The traditional earthenware dishes do not give a very white salt.

Enamel dishes would be good but are too expensive. Instead, rectangular-shaped dishes made from scrap metals and oil drums are used. These are made locally and are always available.

The women salt producers have become technical and scientific experts at extracting high quality salt from silt.

▲ *The improved rectangular funnel.*

▲ *Boiling off the water in an improved metal dish over the protected fireplace.*

The process requires skills, knowledge and understanding. The women have developed the plastering skills needed to make an efficient filter lining.

They have learnt how to control the fire and the boiling process to heat the brine so that only salt crystallizes. The bitter-tasting magnesium salts also found in sea water are left in solution and can be poured off. The women taste the salt – a sensitive and accurate way of checking that they have produced a high quality product that will sell well.

Skills are handed down from mother to daughter, mostly by watching and practising. Knowledge spreads between villages as people visit each other and inter-marry.

Research
Find out what other salts are found in sea water and how they are used. Your science teacher may be able to help you.

Attempts were made by the Sierra Leone Government to introduce large-scale salt processing. These failed due mainly to environmental and technical problems. Local technology has survived through the years, adapting to changing circumstances and becoming more efficient. Its success has been the result of the actions and intelligence of the women themselves.

1 Read through this Case Study again and use the information in it to draw a flow chart showing the new way of producing salt from silt developed by women in Sierra Leone.

▲ *Salt in bags ready for sale.*

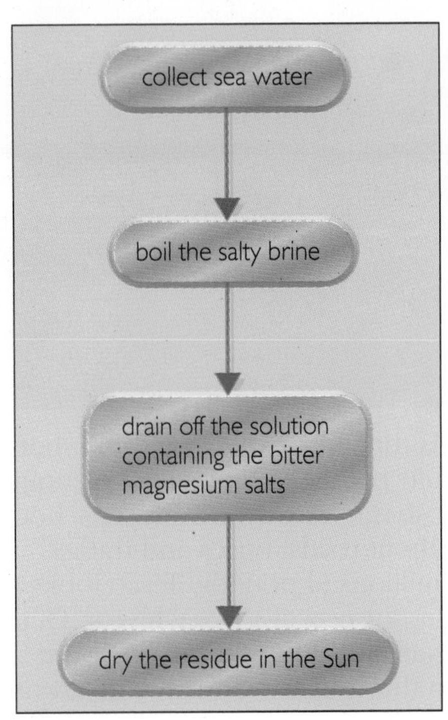

▲ *The steps in the traditional method of producing salt from sea water.*

Comparing the processes

The flow charts show the traditional method of producing salt and how it is produced from the ponds.

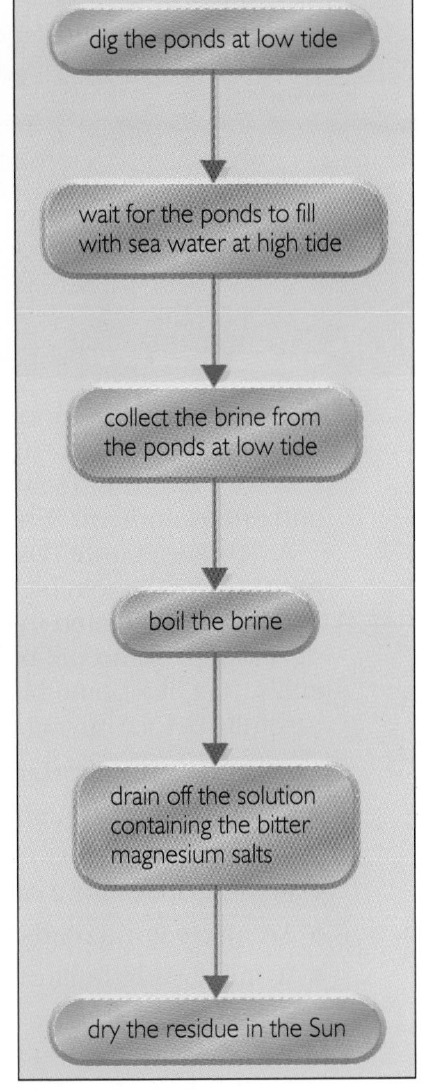

▲ *The steps in producing salt from the ponds.*

18 Siting a superstore – modelling the market

Computer modelling helps sort out the complex information which has to be considered when selecting a site for a new superstore

For most people, a house is the most expensive thing they will ever buy. They think carefully before buying. Is it big enough? Can they afford it? How close is it to the local shops, schools and entertainment? What about roads, buses and trains?

A new superstore costs millions of pounds. Tesco looks at more than 300 possible sites for new stores each year. Of these, 125 will be evaluated in detail and about 20 will finally be developed. Some will be in the country and some in towns and cities. Just like home buyers, Tesco needs to think very carefully before buying a site.

The four most important things the company has to consider are:

- Is the site big enough for a store which carries a large range of products?
- Is there space for a car park and, if possible, a filling station?
- Are there good roads nearby?
- Would a store built on the site be successful?

The first three of these questions can be answered by surveying the site. To answer the fourth question the company needs to be able to predict how successful their store would be if built on the site. **Computer modelling** can help make this prediction.

Pause for thought
What would a company wanting to build a superstore need to know about a site before deciding to buy it?

Computer modelling

Computer modelling uses huge amounts of information collected in a set of databases. Some of this information comes from looking at how well the company's other stores are doing. Some is taken from other sources.

▲ *Using a computer to help Tesco to decide if a site will be successful.*

Evaluating a site

Tesco's Property Department looks for possible new sites for stores all the time. When it finds one which is big enough and near a good road system, it asks the Site Research Department, with its team of Store Location Analysts, to make a sales forecast. This forecast predicts the sales that a store built on the site would make in one week. The computer modelling system they use first works out the total amount of business in the area of the site. Then it works out how much of that business a new store on the site might attract. These predictions are usually accurate to within 10 per cent.

Working out the total business in the area

▲ *Collecting information for computer modelling.*

The first step in predicting sales is to look at the area which surrounds the site – the **catchment area**. How many people live there? How much do they spend on food? How far will they travel to shop? Are these people typical superstore customers?

Research

Survey members of your class. Find out how far their families travel to do their food shopping. Do they travel by foot, public transport or car? Look at the results of your survey and write down any things you have noticed. Make a presentation of your results.

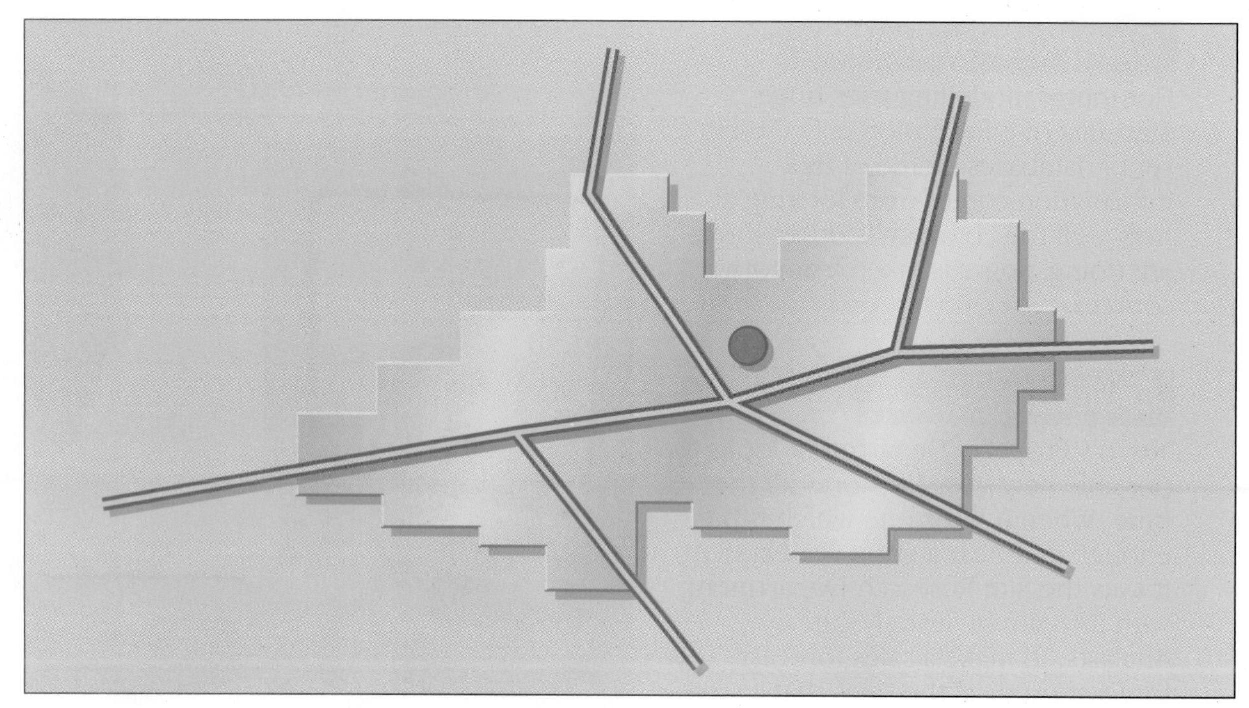

▲ *The catchment area of a proposed site for a superstore.*

Most people drive to their local superstore. To work out the size of a future store's catchment area the Site Research Department uses a road network database. This database contains information about all the roads in the UK. It allows the computer system to work out which places are less than a 15-minute drive away from the site. These places make up the site's catchment area.

The Site Research Department now needs to know how many people live within this catchment area. For this it uses another database, which contains census figures showing the size of the local population, car ownership and household size. Other databases contain information on how much a typical family in the area spends on food. The Site Research Department can use these figures to work out the total amount of money which people in the area around the site spend on food.

The new store's share

The Site Research Department can now predict the total amount which customers in the catchment area spend on food each week. The next step is to decide how many of these customers will use the new store if it is built. To do this it needs to look at the competition. Where else could customers living in the catchment area buy their food? Again, the computer modelling system is used to work this out.

Another database contains details of the locations of all large foodstores. The computer can quickly find all the stores which people in the catchment area could use. The next question is what percentage of people would use the new superstore and what percentage would carry on using existing foodstores.

Research
Schools have catchment areas. A school's customers are its students and their families. How far do members of your class travel to school? Mark their homes on a street map of the area around the school. Draw a catchment area map like the one above. How big is the catchment area for your school?

Pause for thought
What factors might make a customer choose to use one superstore rather than another? Which of these factors are influenced by the site itself?

The size of the superstore, its car park and how easy it is to get to will affect its success. People will travel further to a larger store. People will travel if they know that they will find a parking space.

Each store is like a magnet drawing customers to it. The bigger it is, the better its car parking and the easier it is to get to, the stronger its attraction. The computer model can work out how strong a pull each existing store has on the customers. It can also work out how strong a pull the new superstore would have if it were built. It then looks at all the points within the catchment area and works out whether a customer living there would be pulled towards the new store or stay with a store that already exists. Using this information the computer model can work out what percentage of people in the catchment area would probably shop at the new store.

Q

1 1, 2 and 3 are three existing superstores in this area. Which of these would you expect people living at A, B, C and D to use?

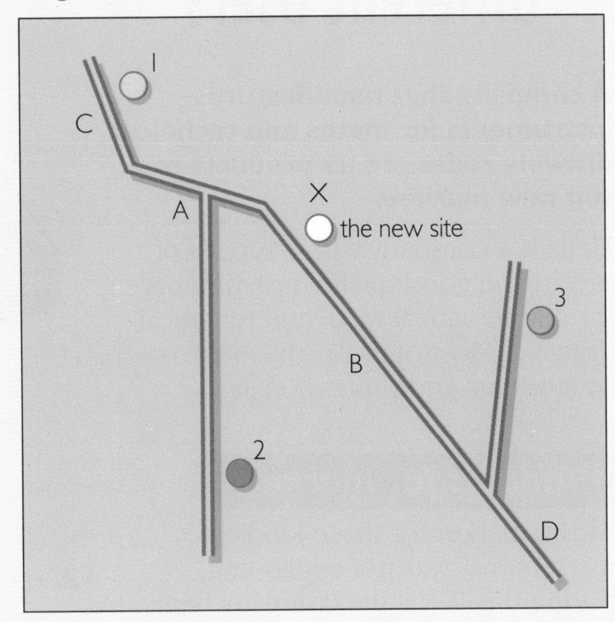

2 If a new store was built at X who might switch to using it? Explain your reasons.

Putting it all together

The Site Research Department now knows:

- the total amount that people in the site's catchment area spend on food each week;
- the percentage of these people who would shop at the new store.

It can now work out how much a superstore built on the site would make in one week if it were to be built! All this information has been worked out using a computer model and information held in databases. All that is needed now is to decide whether the amount of business which the new superstore would do is enough to justify buying the site.

19 Designing maths instruments for different users

A company that manufactures instruments for maths and technical drawing redesigns its products to suit new markets

Helix is a company with a record of producing good quality instruments for mathematical work and technical drawing. Most of its products are used by students and professionals.

▲ *Helix products for technical drawing.*

Products for markets

As the market for these kinds of instruments was not expanding, during the 1980s the company began to manufacture other products. Novelty drawing and writing materials were a growth area so the company decided to make this kind of product as well as the traditional instruments. In particular, there was a big market for products that were linked to a popular film, television series, place or event. A picture or name of the famous person or thing is used to help sell the product. This is called **merchandising**.

▲ *Novelty and merchandised products made by Helix and their competitors.*

Products to meet a new need

In 1988 and 1989 major changes were happening in schools. In maths the changes meant that even young children in primary schools would need to use instruments.

Pause for thought

Look at the instruments in the photograph at the top of the previous page. How would these instruments need to be changed so that 7-year-olds could use them ?

▲ *A young child drawing circles with an ordinary compass.*

The company decided that this was an ideal opportunity to develop in an area it was good at – designing and producing high quality, special drawing instruments. But it had to make products suitable for younger schoolchildren. It carried out some research and identified these problems:

- **Rulers** – A ruler that fits in a pencil case is too short for many jobs. A longer ruler is difficult to store. It may not fit in your bag and often gets broken or damaged.
- **Compasses** – Young children find it easier to use two hands when they are drawing circles with a compass, but then the circle often goes wrong.

1 Can you design a ruler that would fold in half? Use sketches to illustrate your ideas.

2 How could you design a compass which young children could use with both hands without changing the radius of their circle? Use sketches to illustrate your ideas.

The new designs

A folding ruler

The company came up with the idea of a folding ruler. Polypropylene plastic was used for the hinge because:

- it would not need a complicated join as it can be bent without snapping;
- it could fold out quite flat when the ruler was open, and so could be used to draw straight lines;
- it would be simple and therefore cheap to produce;
- the hinge piece 'snaps' off and on the ruler.

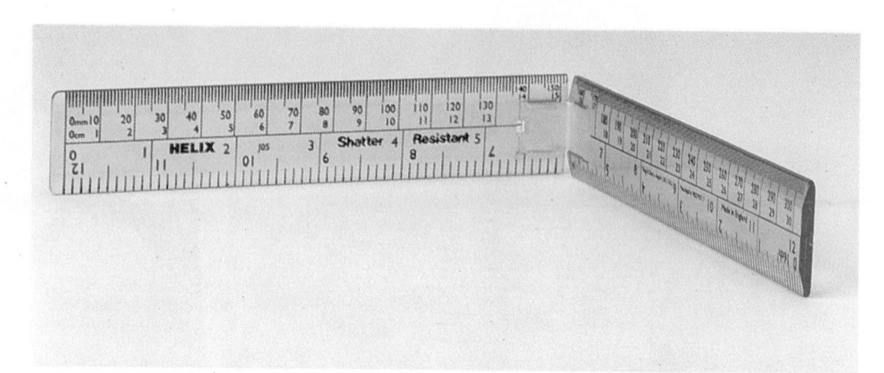

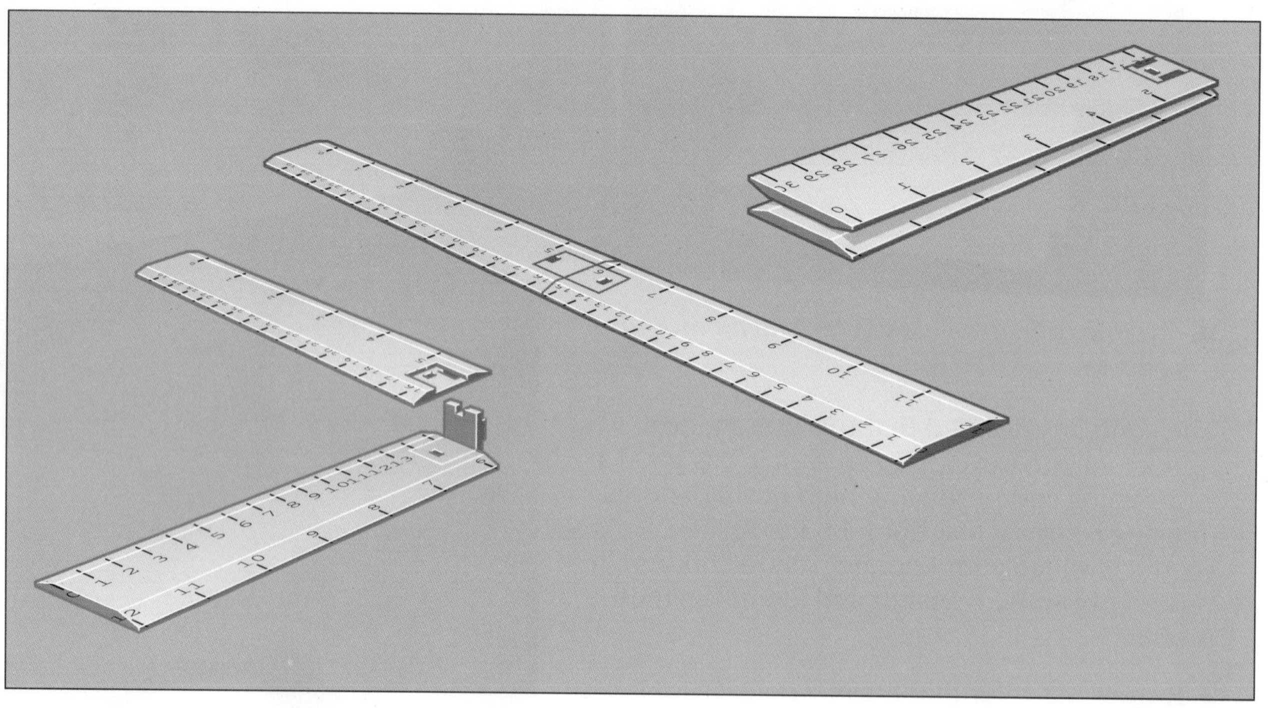

▲ *The new folding ruler.*

A beam compass

The company adapted a beam-designed compass for older children so that it could be used by younger children. Polystyrene plastic was used for the compasses because:

- each part could be moulded to its exact shape – this makes it easy to assemble and use;
- it could be coloured;
- it is strong, light and long-lasting.

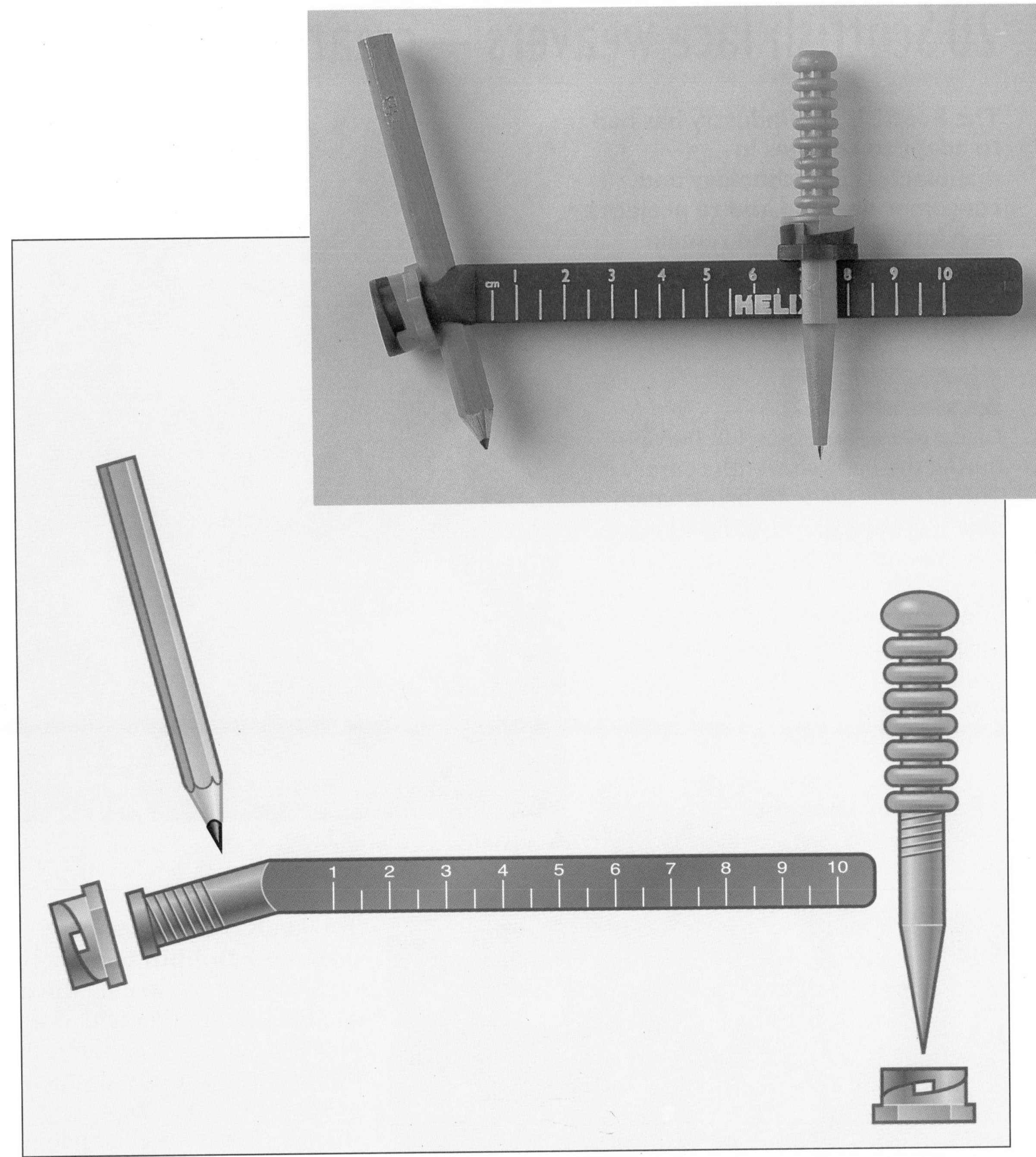

▲ *The new beam compass.*

Other features of the design are:

- the part you hold, to keep the compass still, is shaped for easy grip;
- the beam is marked in centimetres so that you can draw a circle to the size you want;
- the pencil can be adjusted, taken out and sharpened or changed for a ball-point pen or marker.

1 The maths instruments have been redesigned for different users. Who gains and who loses? List the winners and losers explaining how each group of people gained or lost from this activity.

20 Scottish lace weavers – creating a new image

The Scottish lace industry has had to adapt to changes in manufacturing technology and consumer demand and to project a new image in order to remain successful in the face of mass production

▲ *A bobbin lace maker.*

Lace making

Lace making developed in Europe during the early sixteenth century. The lace was made by hand, which meant it was expensive. Hand-made lace was very popular amongst rich people. Most of the paintings in museums and galleries dating from the sixteenth to the early twentieth century show people wearing lace, usually as some kind of trimming – collars, cuffs or edgings.

Pause for thought
Where do you see lace these days?

▲ *Needlepoint lace.*

Two kinds of hand-made lace were produced. **Bobbin lace** was made on a cushion by twisting threads around one another and around pins arranged into patterns, like flowers. It was nearly always made in strips or into collar or cuff shapes. (It is also called pillow lace because it is made on a pillow or cushion.)

Needlepoint lace was produced by embroidering patterns onto fine hand-made cloth or net. This type of lace could be made in much larger pieces, for example for a skirt, wedding veil or table cloth. In the nineteenth century people started using machine-made net as a base. This meant that lace could be produced much more cheaply and so more people could afford it.

Machine-made lace

The Industrial Revolution brought changes in manufacturing techniques. Machines were invented to do the jobs that had been carried out by hand. The textile industry was one of the first to change in this way, with the introduction of **power looms** worked by steam engines. Later, in the early nineteenth century, 'jacquard' looms were invented. These looms could be programmed to produce a wide variety of patterns using sequences of holes punched into cards.

▲ *Machine lace making in Scotland in the 1870s.*

Jacquard looms were the first programmable machines, the forerunners of today's computer-controlled machines.

Research
Find out about jacquard cards and other ways of controlling machines. Produce a display showing how programmable machines have developed.

In Nottingham this process was adapted to weave patterns onto net, resulting in the first lace-making machine. These machines were introduced into textile factories in Ayrshire during the 1870s and quickly became an expanding, profitable part of the textile industry. Several towns in the Ayrshire valleys already had well-developed cotton-weaving industries. The introduction of lace machines enabled the industry and the local communities to grow. During this century the production of machine-made cotton lace has been the main source of employment in the area.

▲ *The big lace factories in Ayrshire in the 1960s.*

The designs for the lace were drawn out onto graph paper and then transferred to the punched cards that controlled the machines.

Computer technology now can be used to produce the patterns and to control the machines. When the cloth is finished it has to be checked for faults. As it is still an expensive product this quality control is important to ensure that the end product is perfect.

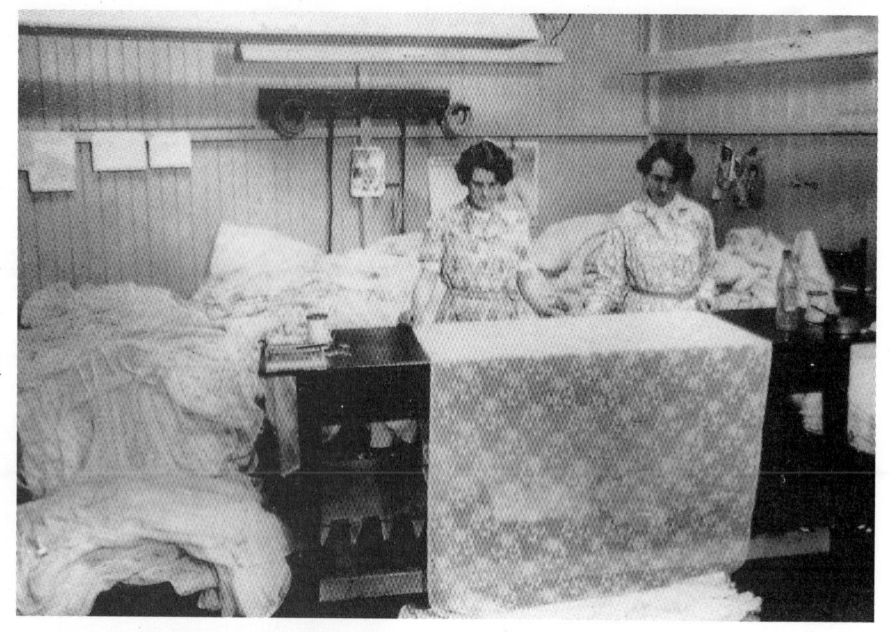

▲ *Checking for faults in the finished lace cloth.*

Problems for the Ayrshire lace industry

Different kinds of thread can be used to make lace. Cotton was the most popular fibre before synthetic fibres were developed. Mixtures with polyester are now most common. They can be woven faster, which makes them cheaper, and the finished goods are easier to care for.

Some Ayrshire weavers changed to producing lace with polyester in order to compete with the cheaper lace made in the large factories in Nottingham and abroad. The Scottish factories, many small, family-owned firms, were trying to sell to their traditional customers and finding it more and more difficult to compete.

Pause for thought
Can you think of any other industries which have had similar problems? What did they do?

The Scottish Development Agency was brought in to try to save this failing industry. They called in a team of management consultants to help them work out what could be done.

▲ *Modern machinery for making lace.*

The management consultants looked into how the lace was being sold and who was buying it. They discovered that often the lace was bought by other companies who repackaged it and then sold it for a lot more money. Perhaps if the manufacturers packaged their own products well enough they could sell them for more and avoid the middle-men.

They also found that the Scottish lace makers were trying to compete with all lace makers, even ones which mass-produced lace on a very large scale. Perhaps they should stop trying to compete with the very big manufacturers. If the Scottish lace makers highlighted that their product was made by skilled workers in a traditional way, they might sell Scottish lace in more specialist shops at higher prices.

They concluded that there were some good things about Scottish lace that could help sell it. If people who bought lace could be persuaded to buy a special, traditional product then the Scottish lace-making companies might not go out of business. So a design company was employed to come up with a new image and identity for the Scottish lace industry.

DESIGN BRIEF

- Develop an image for Scottish lace that will make both trade buyers (who buy things for shops) and the general public think of Scottish lace as a special and high quality product;
- create an identity which could be used to advertise and label all Scottish lace products (alongside the name of each lace manufacturer).

Make use of these special qualities of Scottish lace to help sell it:

- exclusive (only available in selected shops);
- quality craftsmanship (the way that it is made is extremely good);
- heritage (it is a traditional product which has been made in the same way for a long time);
- Scottish (it comes from a country with a strong national identity).

PROJECT OUTLINE

Main stages:

research,
design work,
presentation to clients,
final artwork and production,
delivery of finished items.

Main items produced:

- a packaging identity – something to put in or on all Scottish lace products, such as a sticker or label;
- a brochure – if possible suitable for both trade buyers and individual buyers.

Creating a new image

The Scottish Development Agency invited Drawing Board, a company of designers, to come up with a proposal for developing a new image for all the Scottish lace manufacturers.

The brief

The design company's brief is shown above.

Project outline

The design company produced a plan for the way it would work and what it would produce.

A time schedule was worked out to show how long was to be spent on each part of the project and detailed costings to show how much each part would cost. Once this was accepted, the company had ten weeks to do the work.

The project

First, two designers carried out research into the lace industry and its market. They visited factories to find out how the lace was made and talked to the workers about their ideas and feelings. They visited shops and trade buyers to discover what affected buyers' choice. Was it the price, the look of the packaging, the design of the lace, how easy it was to buy…?

Next came the design phase. They bought a range of other manufacturers' lace products to compare their packaging designs. Then they produced some sketches based on the special qualities of Scottish lace. They had to come up with at least two good ideas that could be presented to the clients. Some of their artwork ideas are shown below.

▲ *Some lace products for different markets.*

▲ *Possible design ideas for Scottish lace.*

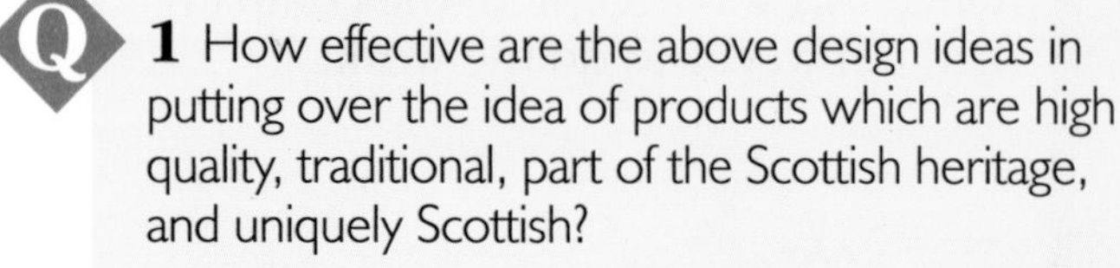

Q **1** How effective are the above design ideas in putting over the idea of products which are high quality, traditional, part of the Scottish heritage, and uniquely Scottish?

▲ *A label that says quality.*

▲ *Promoting the idea of quality.*

2 What methods have the designers used to try to give a feel of quality and Scottish style in the brochure photographs?

3 Where else might they want to use their brand identity?

4 Why do you think they have chosen green for the background colour?

5 What other ways can a label be put on a package?

6 How well do you think the logo fits in with the company letterhead?

7 What other things could be designed to promote Scottish lace?

21 Developing a new product

From the first idea for a new product to its launch, the development process is a team effort in which each member has a special part to play

Businesses grow by identifying new ideas for products and meeting new needs. The superstore chain, Tesco, has sixty product teams developing ideas and working with food suppliers to launch over 1000 new products a year. Each product will have been checked for quality at every stage in its development. Each member of the team has a part to play in making sure that the product is a success.

Pause for thought
Think about all the things that would need to be done to develop a new food product. How big a team would be needed to do this? What might each team member do?

Introducing the team

In the past a single person might have come up with an idea for a product and develop, produce and sell it. Today it is more complicated, and design technologists work in teams. Each team member is an expert in one area and has a specific job to do. Together, the team knows more about the product development process than any individual team member could.

Let's meet the members of a real product team.

- **The product evaluation officer** – 'I work with the other members of the team to develop a product with the right taste, texture and appearance. I need to coordinate the work of the other team members to make sure that the product is acceptable to our customers and of the best possible quality, when it is sold and after it has been stored and then cooked by the customer.'

- **The marketing manager** – 'I make sure that customers will want to buy the new product. Is there a gap in the market? Are there trends in the kinds of food people are buying? Does the new product fit in with our existing products and our marketing strategy?'

- **The buyer** – 'I need to find a supplier who will be able to produce the volume of product we need, as quickly and cheaply as possible without sacrificing quality. I then negotiate terms with them. I will work closely with the food technologist to maintain a good relationship with the supplier.'

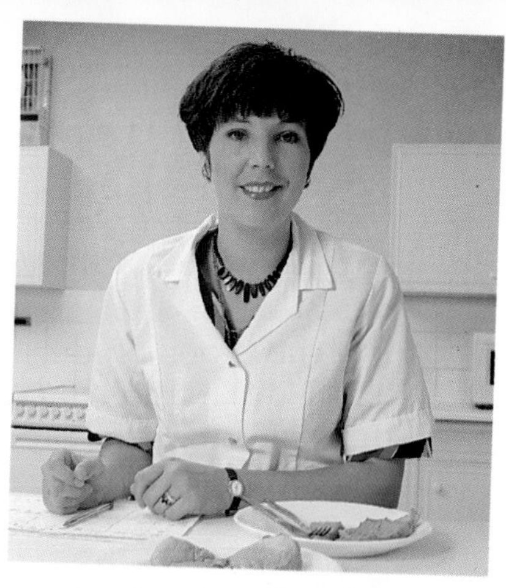

- **The food technologist** – 'I work with the supplier to make sure the product is of the right quality. This involves inspecting raw materials and production processes and advising on the problems which often occur when kitchen samples are scaled up for factory production. The product specification is my responsibility.'

- **The design executive** – 'Most people are first attracted to products by their packaging. My job is to produce attractive packaging and to make sure that it shows all the necessary information, such as the ingredients and nutrition information tables.'

- **The microbiologist** – 'People are naturally worried when they read about bacteria such as listeria and salmonella. I check the product to make sure it does not contain bacteria that could make the consumer ill or that would make it go bad before its use-by date.'

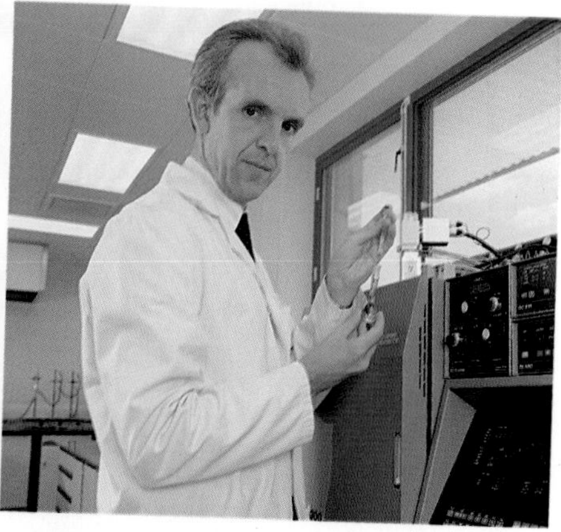

- **The chemist** – 'I check the product for two things. Firstly, is it legal? For example, if the product is advertised as 'low fat', I need to test the product to find out the amount of fat in it. Secondly, is it safe? There must be no trace of dangerous chemicals.'

1 Read through the roles of each member of the team. Discuss and then write down the particular skills and knowledge that each team member needs.

2 What advantages can you see in this type of team?

3 What problems might there be for the team? How might these problems be solved?

Now we are going to see how the team goes about developing a new product.

The product development process

Each new food product passes through several stages from initial idea to launch. This process is designed to make sure that only successful products reach the superstore shelves. No one can guarantee success, but evaluating the product at every stage greatly reduces the risk of failure.

Pause for thought

What might happen if an unsuccessful product is launched? How might it influence the customers? What might be the consequences for the retailer?

▲ *All these products started as ideas.*

The initial idea

Initial ideas for new food products come from various sources. Consumer research might have shown a gap in the market for a higher quality version of a basic product or a cheaper version of an expensive product. Competitors might have launched a new product which is doing well. There may be a consumer trend, for example towards buying healthier products.

A brainstorming session produces a list of possible new products. These ideas might be good or bad. The next part of the process is to examine the potential of each idea.

1 Think about the products you can buy in a large superstore. List any new products which have appeared on the shelves.

2 Do you notice any trends in these new products? For example, are there trends in the type of food, its packaging or its intended market?

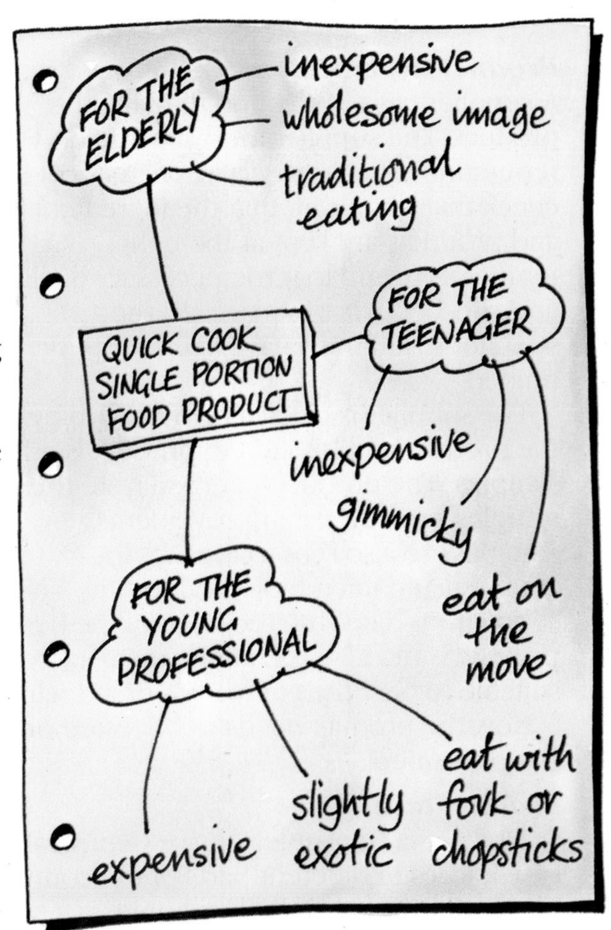

▲ *Ideas for new food products from a brainstorming session.*

▲ *The checklist used to screen an idea for a new product.*

Concept screening

Each idea needs to be looked at in detail.

- Will the product be popular with the customers?
- Does it match the company's quality image?
- Will it reduce the sales of other goods in the store?
- Can it be made in bulk?
- Does it look attractive?
- Can it be produced at the right cost?
- Is it the right time of year to launch this product?

If the answer to any one of these questions is 'no' then the idea is rejected. If all the answers are 'yes' the product idea passes on to the next stage.

3 All design technologists need to screen new ideas before developing them. You will be developing many new ideas throughout your design and technology course. Look at the list of questions above.

a Write down those which you could use to screen your own ideas.

b Which do not apply?

c Can you think of any others to add to the list?

Product development

A supplier has to be found to make the product. The supplier must have a good reputation. The factory is inspected to check that it is clean, that the ingredients and products are kept at the right temperature and that the necessary quality control checks are in place. All the supplier's staff must have been properly trained.

The supplier is given a brief describing the product and is asked to produce some samples. The product team will taste these samples and suggest improvements. Samples are also sent to the labs for chemical and microbiological testing. The supplier modifies the recipe until the best product is made which all the team agree is suitable to bear the company's brand name.

Now the product needs to be tested on the consumers.

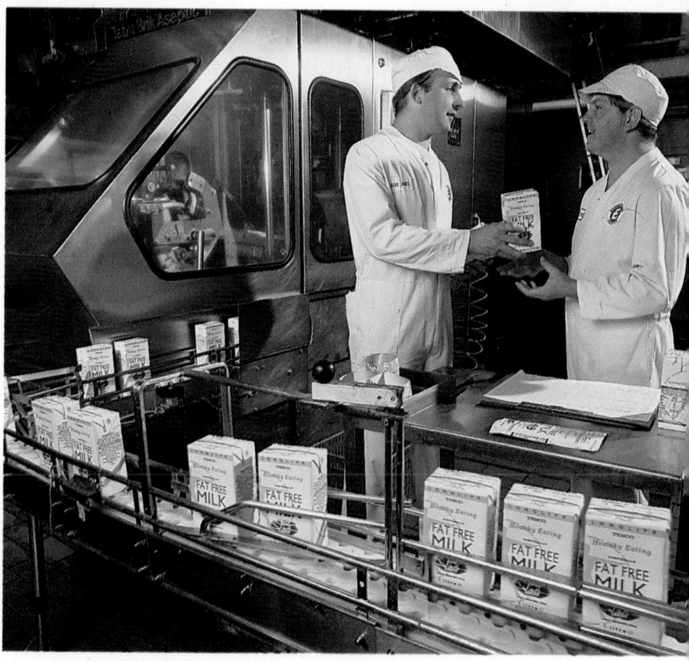

▲ *Inspecting the factory and products of a possible supplier.*

Pause for thought
What things are people looking for when inspecting a food factory?

Product testing

Tesco has six Consumer Advice Centres in superstores in different parts of the country. These centres are staffed by home economists who advise the public and organize consumer-tastings of new products. Customers in the store are asked if they are willing to take part in the market research. It is important to ask the right people: you wouldn't ask pensioners to taste a product aimed at young children.

The people who agree to take part are given samples to taste, usually one of the new product and one of an existing similar product. They are not told which is which. This is called a 'blind' tasting. The customers fill in a questionnaire. They are asked to compare the two products in a variety of ways. One hundred customers in two different stores are asked for their opinions and the results of the survey are fed into a computer. If the new product scores highly in the testing it goes on to the next stage. If the product fails the consumer test the product team and supplier start the product development stage again.

▲ *Customers try out a new product.*

Pause for thought
Why are customers usually asked to compare two products? Why are they not told which is which? Why is research carried out at two different stores?

Pack design

The new product needs to be packaged. A sample of the product is tested to find out all the nutritional information needed for the pack. Photographs of the product are taken and artwork produced. Cooking instructions are written along with suggested ways of serving the product.

Meanwhile the supplier is preparing to make the product in bulk.

▲ *Attractive, informative and effective packaging is very important to the success of a product.*

The first production run

The supplier now needs to convince the team that they are ready to go into full production. Up to now the samples used in the tests may have been produced in special kitchens at the suppliers. The final product will be produced on a production line. Under supervision, the supplier organizes a first production run of the product. This will last half a day, which is long enough to show that the product can be produced consistently to a high standard.

The launch

The product is now ready to be launched, but this is not the end of the story. The team will be looking at the product regularly to check its quality, to see whether people are buying it and whether it could be developed further.

▲ *A new product on the production line.*

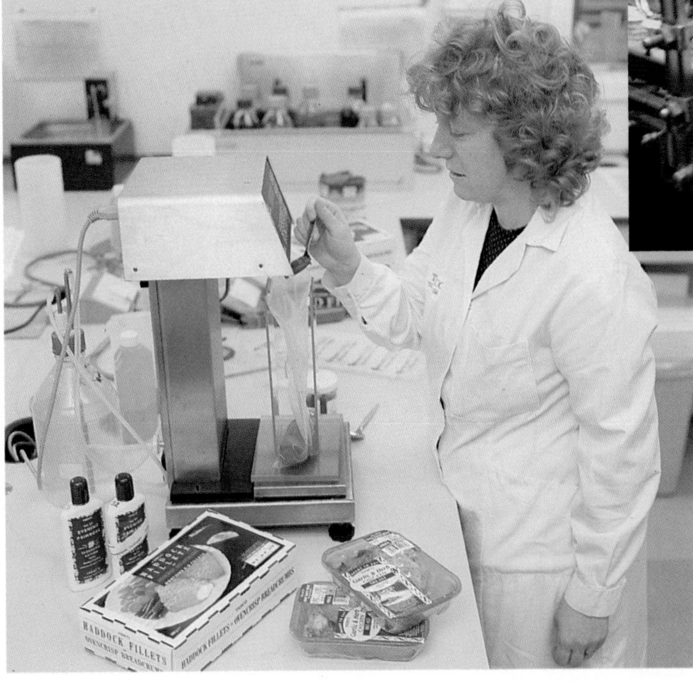

▲ *A new product's quality being checked.*

1 Look back at the roles of the team members. Which team members are involved at each stage of the product development process?

2 Make a chart showing what each team member does at each stage of the process.

4 SCHOOLS

22 Inventing is only the start

Inventing is only part of the story of a successful product

Some inventions start as bright ideas, some are discovered, often by chance during work on other things, and some are the result of painstaking research and development.

Inventing is a rare thing. We cannot all do it – although often we would like to! The frustration of knowing that you need something special to do a particular job, or that there must be an easier or better way of doing something, often sets off inventive thoughts.

Pause for thought
What makes an inventor?

Here are some of the qualities or skills an inventor may have or need:

Cat's-eyes – Percy Shaw's invention has saved thousands of lives. ▶

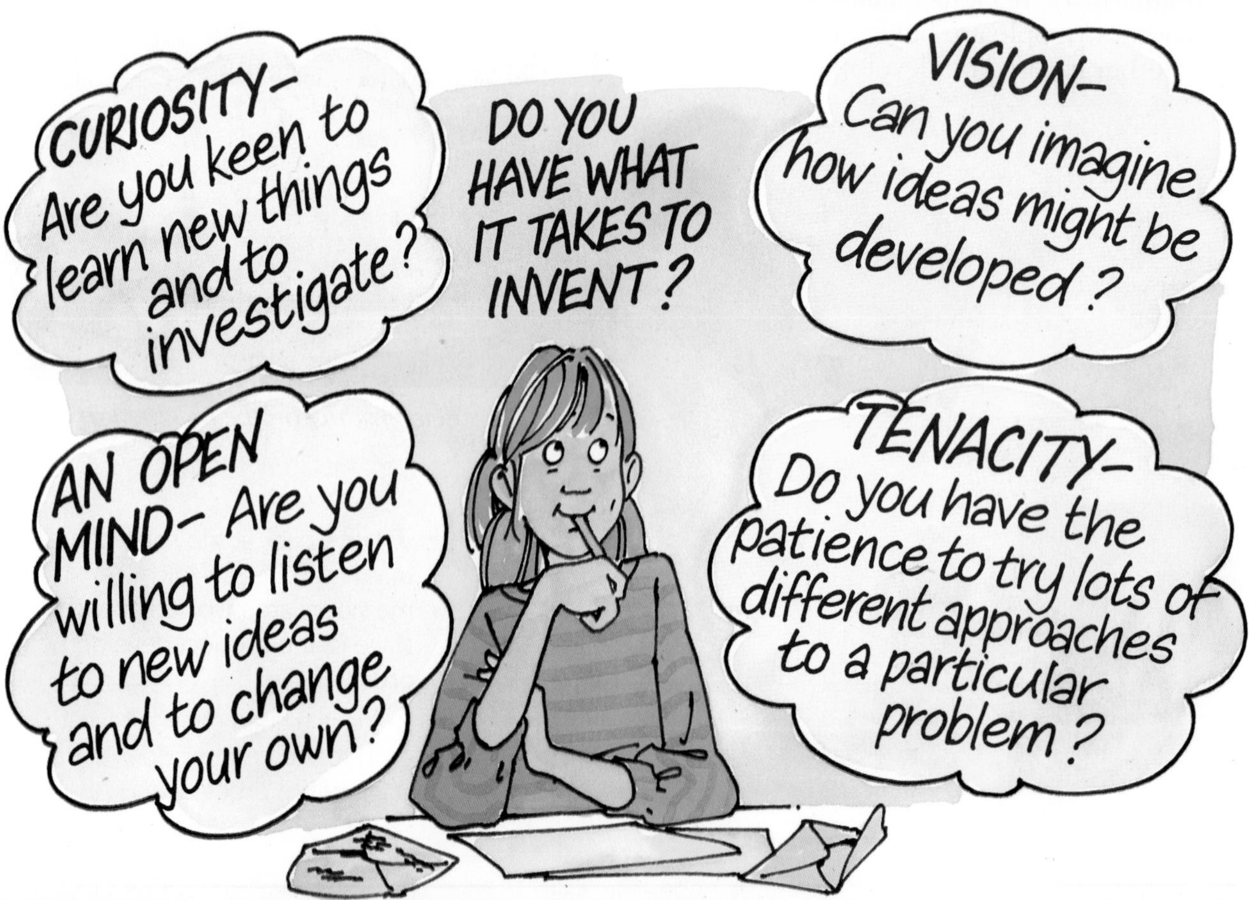

What makes for successful inventing?

A successful invention is not produced by just one person. Getting your bright idea produced and into the hands of the people who will use it or need it, involves many other people.

People who make an invention a success

The manufacturing and production team develop and oversee the production processes.

Designers and engineers develop the idea so it is safe, can be manufactured and is easy to use.

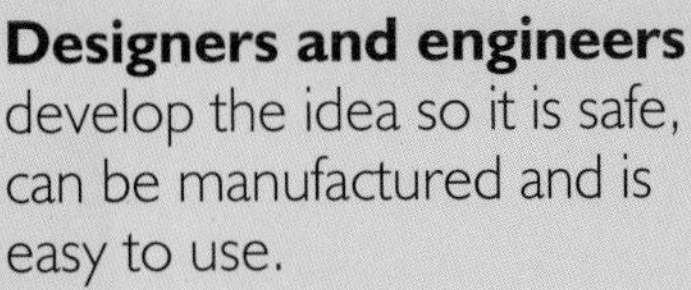

The marketing and advertising team work out who is likely to buy the product, how many are likely to be sold, how best to advertise it and where to sell it.

Retailers – products are sometimes manufactured and sold by the same company. This means they can control how the product is presented to customers in shops.

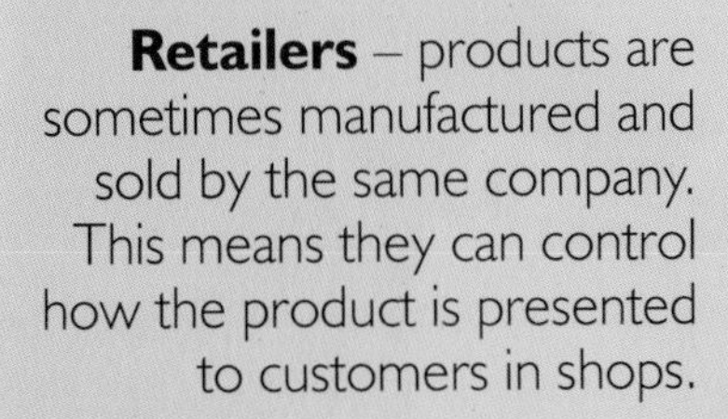

Where do failures fit in?

The C5 was invented by Sir Clive Sinclair. He designed it for people to use as local transport, but it did not sell. The driver sits in the vehicle and uses either an electric motor or pedals for power. This is an improvement on a bicycle but not quite as convenient as a car. It was a complete commercial failure. After ten months, C5 production was stopped. Sir Clive put this failed project down to experience and carried on with his work. He still wanted to produce the electric vehicle for the future. By keeping up with the latest technology he developed his idea for an electric bike, the Zike. Sinclair fans are convinced that he is moving towards a revolution in personal transport.

Easy *to use*

Cheap *to run*

Environmentally *friendly*

Ideal for *short local trips*

The selling points of the C5.

1 Work with a partner. You are a marketing assistant for Sir Clive Sinclair, and your partner is the director of a large chain of cycle stores. Use the information in the panels to convince your partner that the Zike will be much more successful than the C5 and that his or her stores should stock it. After a few minutes, swap roles. List the good and bad points of an electric bicycle.

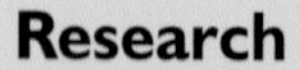

Research

Find out how cat's-eyes in roads work and why they are not damaged when a car travels over them. Present your answer as a labelled sketch.

Fun *to ride*

Cheap *to run*

Environmentally *friendly*

Uses latest battery *and motor technology*

Takes the work *out of cycling*

The selling points of the Zike.

Moving on

The Zike's technology can be used to give an ordinary bicycle electric power. The Sinclair Zeta uses the same electric motor as the Zike and one rechargeable battery. It fits neatly onto the back of any bicycle.

2 Why did Sir Clive Sinclair bother to develop the Zeta?
3 What are the advantages of having the Zeta *and* the Zike in the market-place?
4 What are the disadvantages of having them both in the market-place?

▲ *A simple belt drive transmits power in the Sinclair Zeta.*

5 Here is a range of items that have been invented to make office work easier. List all the items shown.
6 For each one decide how useful it would be for helping you do your homework and for keeping your school work in order. Give each one a rating on a 5-point scale: 5 points for very useful to 1 point for not useful at all.
7 Now think of something to do with homework and organizing your school work that isn't covered by your list. Perhaps you can invent something to help!

Television link: *Tectactics* – The Designer's Story

23 It's only where I wash

A lot of design work goes into our bathrooms and the products we use in them

The changing face of bathrooms

Most of us take the bathroom for granted, but not so long ago people had to use outside toilets and public baths. Then a bathroom was a definite luxury that only the wealthy could afford.

Pause for thought

Imagine if all the fittings in your bathroom were transparent. You would see pipes everywhere. A lot of thought has gone into the arrangement of the pipes that bring in fresh water and the waste pipes that take waste away to the sewage plant.

▲ *This bathroom is old and for the rich.*

Most houses or flats now have bathrooms and we are used to turning on the tap and having instant water. When we pull out the plug or flush the toilet, the waste is disposed of 'invisibly'.

Many modern bathrooms include showers, either over baths or as a separate unit, and some include a bidet. Some busy homes have two wash-basins – particularly useful when everybody is trying to get ready at the same time!

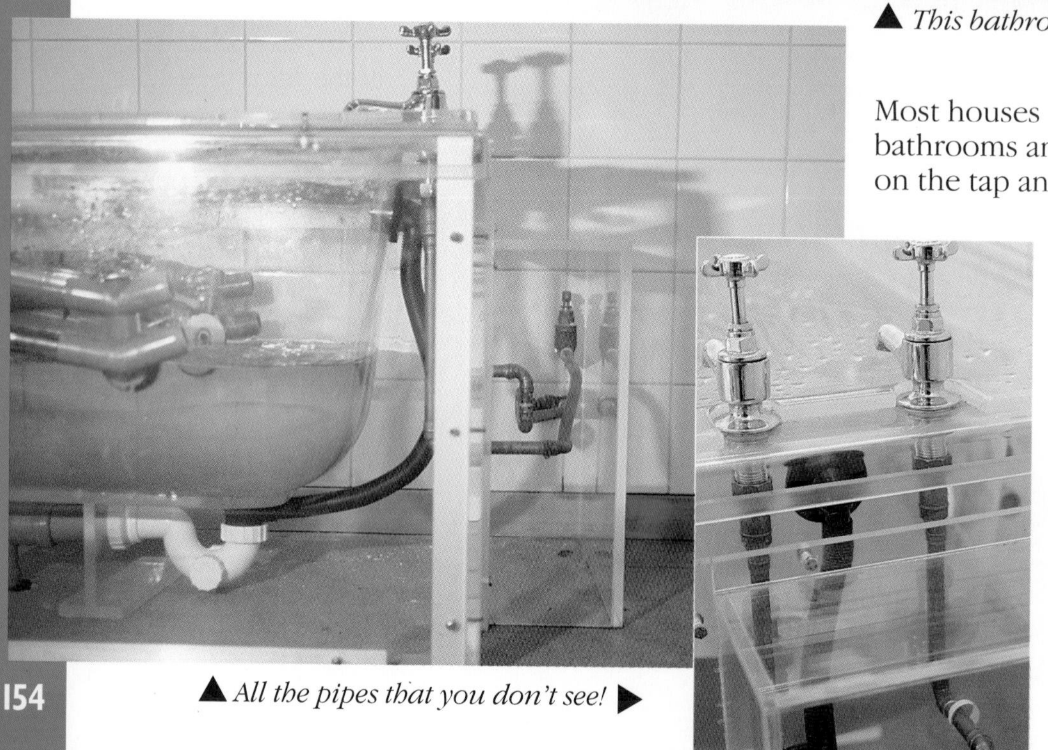

▲ *All the pipes that you don't see!* ▶

What has brought about these changes?

- Builders now include fully-fitted bathrooms in new houses and in houses they are doing up. So almost everyone has a bathroom in their home.
- The introduction of cheaper materials for mass production has meant that good quality furniture and fittings can be bought at reasonable prices.
- Fittings and accessories for bathrooms are now available in most DIY stores. So many people can improve their own bathrooms.
- Today, more people travel overseas than 20 or 30 years ago. In their travels, particularly to hotter climates, they see different types of fittings and think about including them in their own bathrooms, for example showers and bidets.

Bathrooms can be designed in various shapes and sizes. ▶

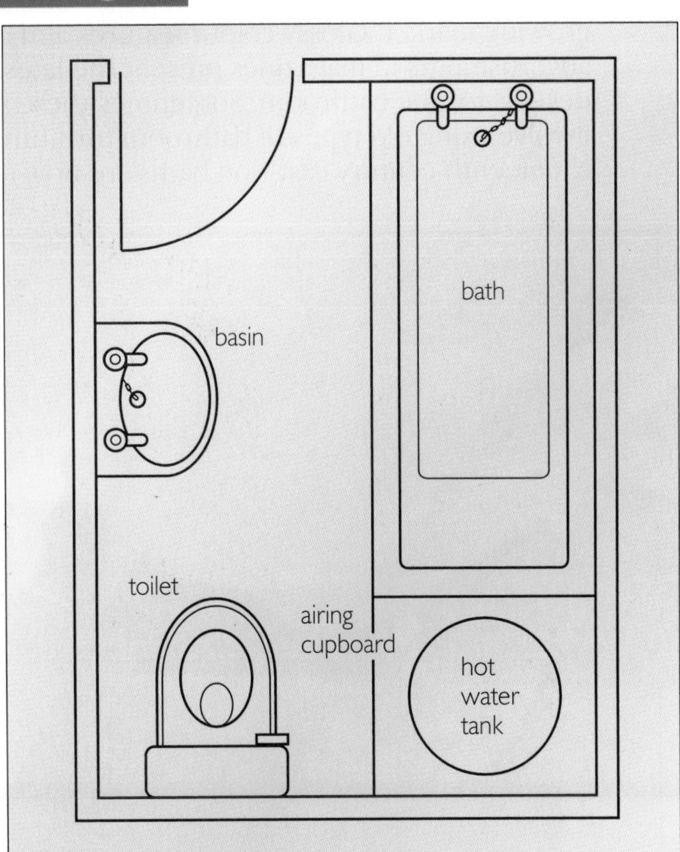

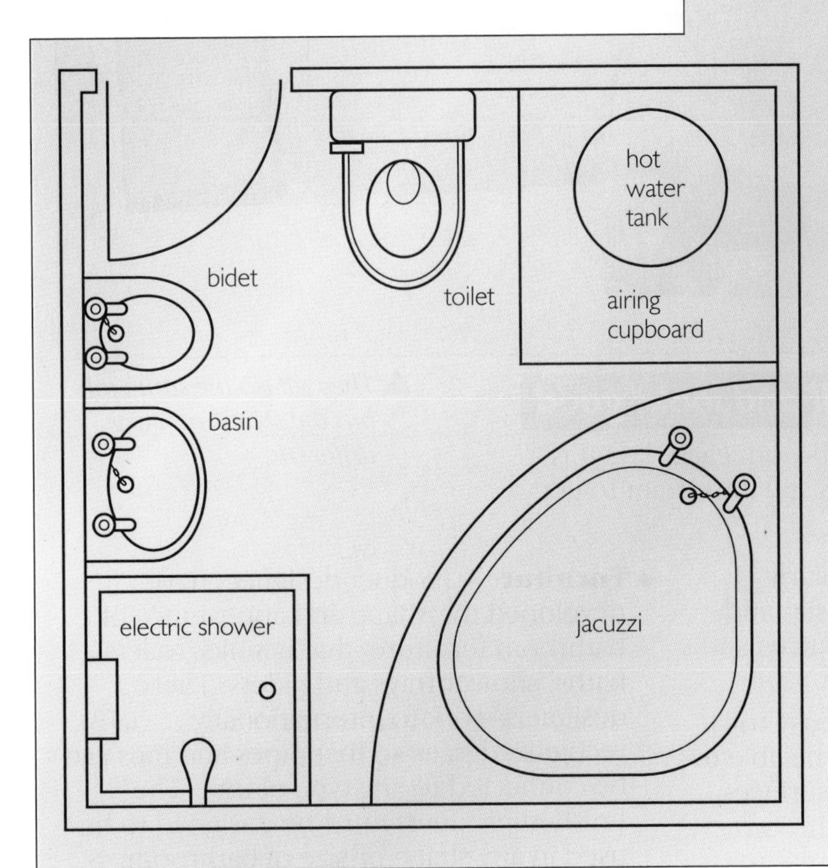

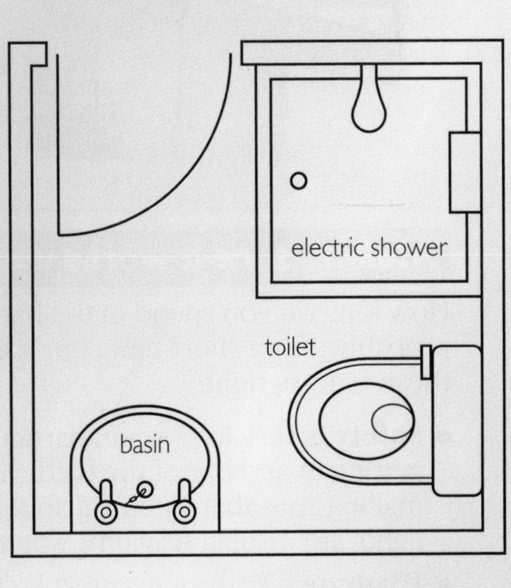

People now want more than the basic bathroom. Designers and manufacturers have responded to this growing market. Glossy colour features and advertisments in magazines present the latest 'look' or designs for the bathroom. Sometimes these looks involve using old types of bathroom furniture. Nineteenth century cast-iron baths are now all the rage!

Research
Find pictures of bathrooms in old magazines. Develop a display showing the wide ranges of bathroom furniture and fittings now available.

▲ *They all do the same job but the styles are very different.*

Making sure it works well and looks good

How long do you spend in the bathroom each day? It is probably only a short time, but it is still important to get these aspects right:

- **Safety** is very important, particularly getting in and out of the bath easily, and making sure that electrical appliances and lights are insulated against water.
- **Hygiene** – Bathrooms must be easy to clean and maintain. You need to be able to clean fixed furniture, floors and surfaces easily. The materials used for bathroom suites vary from plastics, to ceramics to enamelled cast-iron. They are all easy to keep clean.
- **Furniture** – Product designers have developed the shape and appearance of bathroom furniture, that is sinks, toilets, baths, shower trays and bidets. These designers work to internationally recognized sizes so that pipes and taps can be connected to any type of unit. The finished products must be designed to be used in any shape or size of bathroom.

Products to use in the bathroom

There is a huge variety of products to help us keep clean and fresh. For instance, you can buy shower products that form part of a complete range including soap, talcum powder, deodorant and body lotion. Others are intended to be used on their own; they are 'stand-alone' products. Many shower products can also be used to wash hair, so cutting down the number of items you need to have. There's definitely no need for a slippery bar of soap!

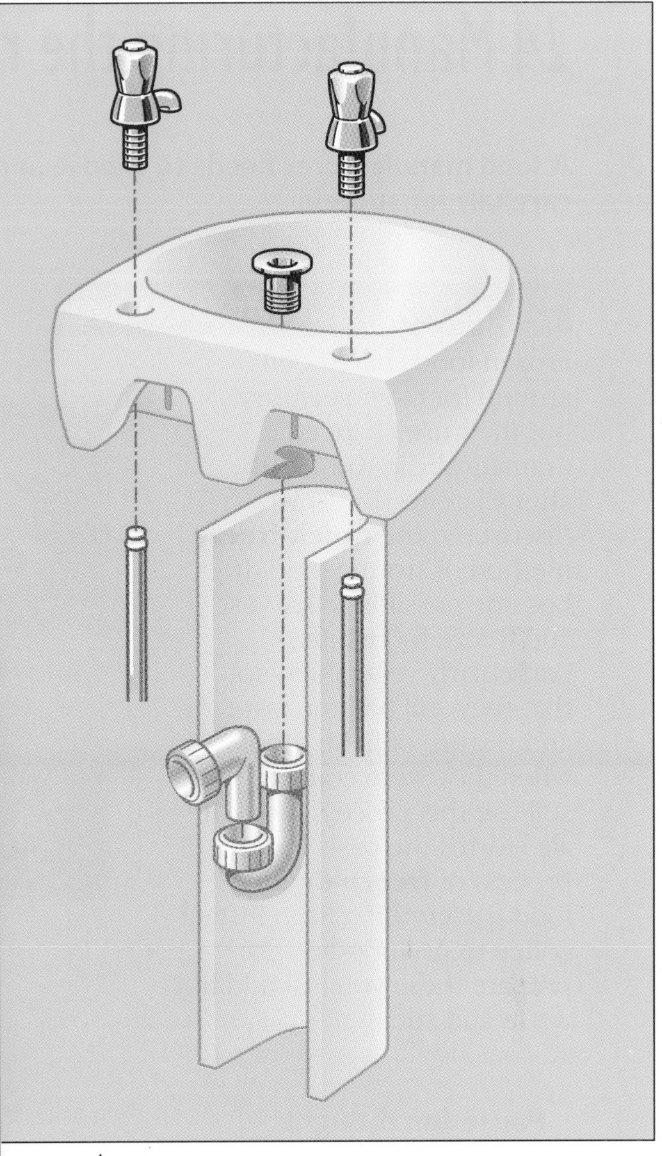

▲ *All these parts must be designed to fit together and be leakproof.*

▲ *All these to wash ourselves!*

1 List bathroom activities. For instance, getting dressed or undressed, cleaning teeth, treating spots.

2 List the things you need to carry out each activity. For instance, for getting dressed or undressed you might need clothes' hooks on the door and a dirty-washing basket; for treating spots you need spot cream, a mirror, good light, clean hands (so a soap and a towel) and perhaps cotton wool.

3 Work with others to develop a complete list of bathroom products. Discuss whether each of these items is a luxury or a necessity.

24 Manufacturing the right product

A food manufacturer needs to choose and market products carefully for success

Beginning with Mr Birdseye

Frozen foods have been around for over a century but their use changed dramatically in the 1930s after Clarence Birdseye discovered the **quick-freeze** method of storing food. It became possible to harvest and freeze foodstuffs, particularly vegetables, so that they still had the taste and texture of fresh food when they were cooked. We still use this process today. It also forms the basis for the process of **freeze-drying** food – everything from instant coffee to pot noodles. To prepare these you just add hot water and stir.

▲ *The same frozen food but different packaging.*

Pause for thought

Clarence Birdseye's discovery has made frozen foods widely available. They are a type of convenience food – quick and easy to cook. How many times in a week do you eat frozen foods? How often do you eat freeze-dried foods?

What are the important factors for success?

Getting the right product

BCB, a food manufacturer, wants to market freeze-dried products as convenience foods. BCB needs to produce food products that sell well, but how does it decide what to produce? As a first step, BCB looks at existing products. It may find:

- a gap in the market and decide to make a product to fill that gap;
- a product that is already very successful and decide to make a similar product. This will compete with the other product and, if successful, take some of its share of the market.

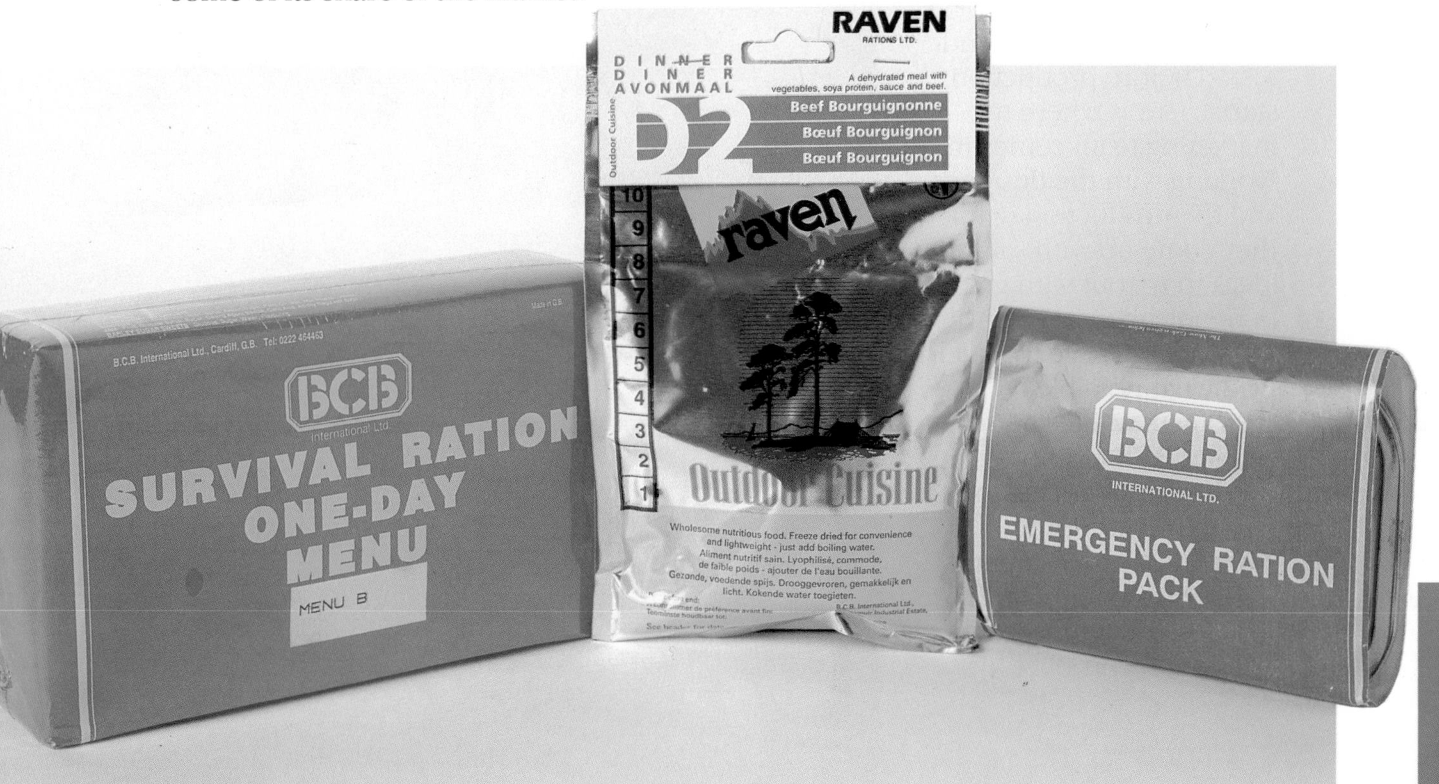

▲ *BCB makes food for expeditions. It will need to change the product* and *the company's image to sell in supermarkets.*

Setting the right price

Once BCB has decided on the product, it has to work out:

- how much it will cost to produce – a **manufacturing cost**;
- how much it can be sold for – a **retail cost**.

Should the product be cheaper or more expensive than its competitors'?

- If it is cheaper, BCB will need to sell more to make a profit. This means persuading people that cheaper means better value, not lower quality.
- If it is more expensive, BCB may make more profit for each item sold but will need to persuade consumers that the product is worth the higher price.

Getting the right appearance

BCB now has to decide how to package its product and what it will look like. It looks at other products on supermarket shelves to see tried and tested ways of presenting similar products.

1 List the four things that BCB must decide about the food products it is going to manufacture.

Marketing

How can BCB be sure that it is on the right track? The ideas have to be tried and tested before production starts. This is where the marketing team comes in. Working with the designers and the production team, they come up with sample ideas to try out with groups of people who are typical customers. These trials tell BCB what possible customers want. This enables BCB to improve its products to meet customer requirements. Some companies spend months, even years, conducting market tests to ensure the success of a product.

▲ *It is packaging that attracts us to food products.*

2 Lasagne is a popular Italian dish but it takes quite a long time to prepare and cook from raw ingredients. It is sold ready-made in many supermarkets. List *everything* shown on the lasagne packaging in the picture on the opposite page.

Divide the items on your list into:

- Information that encourages the consumer to buy the product. This will include the photograph of the dish and the graphics – the things that contribute to the attractiveness of the packaging.
- Information that helps the consumer. This includes information about how to store and cook the product, and how many people it will feed.
- Information that has to be included by law to help and protect the consumer – price, ingredients, weight, sell-by or use-by date and dietary information.
- Information that helps the retailer. This includes barcodes for use with automatic check-outs.

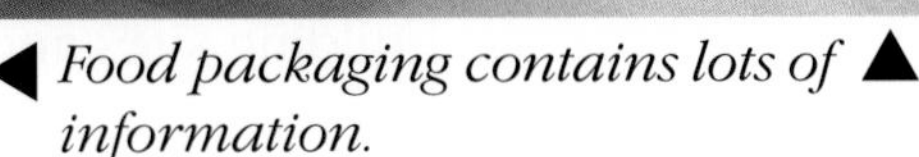

Food packaging contains lots of information.

Research

Imagine that you have been asked to develop a range of new convenience food products on the theme of *Scrumptious Journeys through Europe*.

1 List the food products in your local supermarket that could be part of this range.

2 Note down where in Europe each of these food products comes from.

3 Find other places in Europe which have food specialities that are not on your list.

4 Rough out some ideas showing what the outer package might look like for one or two of these food products.

A team effort

To get this food product to the supermarkets' shelves has involved the work of a large team of people:

- The **market researchers** have established the types of products that customers will buy.
- The **nutritionists** or **home economists** have developed the appropriate recipes. These have been market-tested again. They work with the **manufacturing** and **production teams** to ensure quality in long production runs.
- Meanwhile the **graphic designers** have been working through ideas for the containers and outer packaging. These have also been tested with customers. The graphic designers might commission an **illustrator** or a **photographer** to capture the right image of the dish for the outer packaging. The photographer might have a **stylist** working alongside her/him to get exactly the right 'look', making the image so mouth-watering that the customer cannot resist putting it in their shopping trolley!

25 Making markets

Companies can create markets for new and existing products

When you are next out, take a look around you and see how many people are wearing cycling helmets. If you live in a busy town or city you are likely to see many cyclists wearing helmets. There is more traffic and so more chance of an accident than in quiet areas.

In some jobs and sports, people must wear safety helmets. For instance, on building sites and in sports such as horse riding. Often these have to meet recognized safety standards.

Pause for thought

It is not compulsory for pedal-cyclists to wear helmets. Motorcyclists or horse riders (under the age of 14) are required by law to wear safety helmets if they drive or ride on the roads. Should helmets be compulsory for pedal-cyclists too?

Helmets for city cyclists.

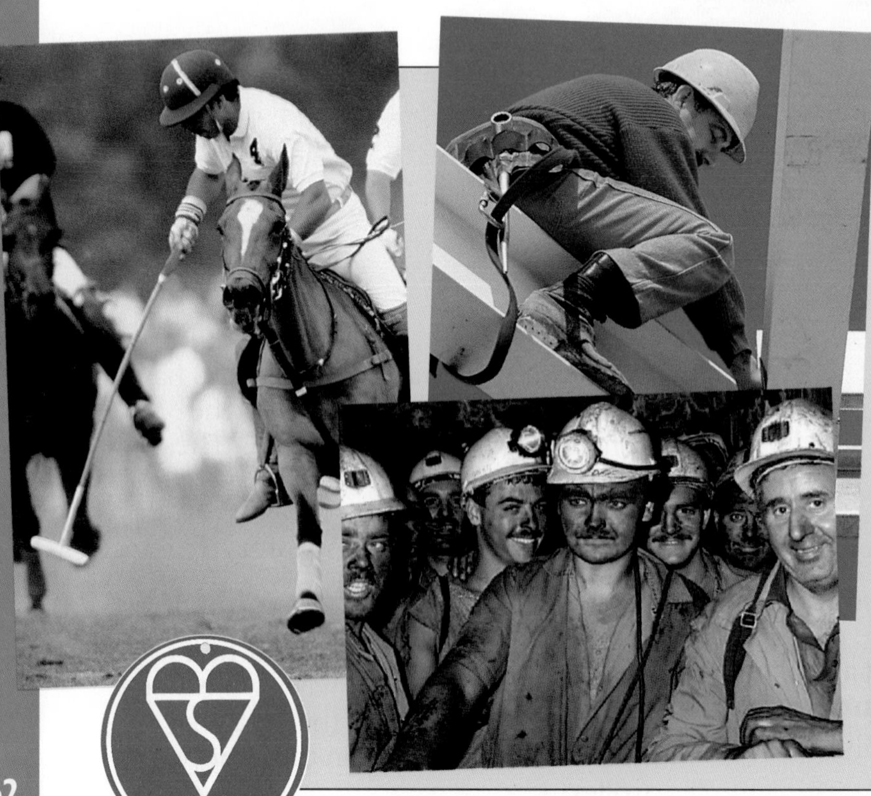

All these helmets must meet safety standards.

Compulsory or voluntary?

People are given lots of information about safety issues. The figures for head injuries resulting from motorcycle accidents should be enough to make anybody want to wear a helmet. But the only way to make sure that all motorcyclists wore helmets was to pass a law to enforce the wearing of crash helmets.

Why should society bother? Apart from being in the motorcyclists' best interests, the cost of accidents to society can be huge. Healthcare for head and other injuries is very expensive. Some survivors might not make a full recovery, and will require continuous and expensive aftercare. So, while we can never stop accidents, we can limit the damage and costs.

▲ *Different helmets for different cyclists.*

Persuading the customer

Most products are not 'compulsory' and people have to be persuaded that they are worth buying. Companies have to convince people that they need or want the product or service they are providing. They do this through **advertising** and **promotion**.

Once a product is successful in one market, new markets can be created by selling to different groups of customers, if they can be persuaded that these products are worth buying. This was the case for cycle helmets. At first these were just for off-road racing, but a wide range of styles has developed. There is a helmet for just about every type of cyclist.

But chocolate melts in the summer …

▲ *Chocolate products for summer time.*

The main problem with chocolate is that it melts in the heat. This makes it sticky in hot weather and sometimes affects its taste and texture. So sales of chocolate products drop dramatically during warm summer months. Chocolate manufacturers plug this gap in the market with ice-cream versions of their best-selling sweets. Then they have steady sales throughout the year.

Pause for thought
Consider these ice-cream sweets. Why did sweet manufacturers move into the ice-cream market?

And what about completely new inventions?

Market researchers carry out the following steps on a new product idea:

- Try out the idea on people.
- Record what they think and tell the rest of the team.
- Get the team to develop the idea according to what people think.
- Test the idea again.

But what about new inventions? Consumers have no experience or knowledge of them. These product ideas are very difficult to try out and test. The Sony Walkman is a good example. When it was launched there was nothing else like it on the market. It challenged people's ideas about how, when and where they might listen to music. Whilst the technology for the product has developed dramatically, enabling the size and weight to be reduced, the basic principle remains the same.

Sony continually reviews and assesses which Walkmans sell well. It drops poor-selling lines and manufactures more of the best-sellers in their place. The Walkman has moved with the times and the changing needs of the consumer. Standard Walkmans now come in a range of sizes and colours and there are now waterproof and even solar-powered versions as well as those with radios!

The Walkman is one of the most successful inventions and product launches of the last two decades.

▲ *The Sony Walkman – a very successful product platform.*

1 For each type of Walkman in the picture, write down who you think would use it.

2 For each of the cycle helmets shown on page 162–3, write down who you think would wear it.

More bright ideas

Some new products are developed to sell another. When the battery company, Duracell, was thinking of products to promote its sales of batteries, it came up with the idea for a new range of torches. These would be free-standing and have a directable beam, even in the smallest versions. They also had to be competitive in price with other torches.

BIB Design Consultants developed the design from the idea through to manufacture. This involved designing a new type of switch mechanism and a whole new look for the torch, now known as the Duracell Colour Pocket torch. This product has now successfully challenged traditional torches on the market for several years.

▲ *A new product for an old market.*

26 Shopping and choice

The way we shop and the choices we have are very different from the time of our grandparents

Do we really have a choice?

In the supermarket, the chemist's or the clothes' shop there are lots of different products to buy. The variety seems endless and it looks as if we have lots of choice. Does a large number of products within one product area, say washing powders, mean that consumers are offered real choice? Not necessarily.

Most washing products are manufactured by two major producers – Proctor & Gamble and Lever Brothers. The products they manufacture are in direct competition with one another. Sometimes they even produce direct competitors to their own products. They do this to gain as large a share of the market for a particular type of product as they can.

Pause for thought

Imagine what it would be like if, when you went shopping, you could only pick from one or two different types of shampoo for your hair, or from just two or three different types of chocolate bar, or from only Cheddar, Double Gloucester or Wensleydale cheeses. This is what shopping was like just a few generations ago.

▲ *Only one manufacturer is involved in producing all these different shampoos.*

The joys of shopping

▲ *Shopping made easy.*

Shopping has changed dramatically over the last 15 years. For household needs there are now supermarkets all over the country. Many more households in the UK now own cars and shoppers can travel to one of the huge superstores on the outskirts of towns. These offer the widest range of goods imaginable, from food and clothes to music and gardening equipment. You can do all your shopping under one roof. You can even buy your petrol and newspapers there.

As a result consumers' expectations have changed. They want their shopping to be easy. They are less prepared to wander from shop to shop seeking the best buys – few shoppers have the time!

Pause for thought

When you go shopping how do you decide what you will buy? Do you have a list on paper or do you just remember? How do you decide between different types of the same product?

Knowing what you want

How do we, as consumers, know what we want? We are given lots of choice in the supermarket and on the high street. Our magazines and television breaks are full of advertisements for the latest products. All the products have been designed to appeal to particular consumer groups.

But how do the designers know what particular groups will like? Many designers use **image boards**. These show the sorts of things that a consumer group already likes and uses. This may include pictures of places and activities as well as products. In this way, they can build up a picture of how a consumer might use the product they are designing and how it will fit into their life style. They may even draw pictures of typical consumers using the product in their everyday life. In this way, the product is designed to appeal to one or more consumer groups.

▲ *This image board tells us about the consumer's preferences.*

Slaves to fashion?

The fashion world works differently. Fashion designers sell the consumer an image or a look. This might have been promoted in magazines and newspapers. Often it is based on high-fashion designs that most of us cannot afford. The original ideas are not the result of market research, although the designers often have a very clear idea of the type of person they are designing for. The market test for the new clothes is their successful sale to stores all over the world.

▲ *Expensive high-fashion designs which influence the design of the clothes in our high street shops.*

Trends in fashion are often set out by fashion journalists. Sometimes fashion trends develop from street culture and music. For instance, the explosive growth in sales of sports shoes as a fashion accessory followed on from the trainer becoming popular with young blacks in the USA, particularly as a dance shoe for hip hop in Detroit.

1 Discuss with other students where you get information about fashion in clothes. Write this up as a list with the title 'Teenage fashion influences'.

2 Rewrite the list with the most important sources at the top and the least important at the bottom.

Research

Investigate the chocolate sweet-bar market.

1 Visit your local newsagent or supermarket and list all the chocolate-based sweet-bars that are on sale. Beside each product write down the name of the manufacturer – Cadbury, Nestlé, Mars, and so on – and the price.

2 Now rewrite the product names in order of increasing price under the heading of the manufacturer.

3 Within each manufacturer's range colour-code those products that appear to be in competition with each other.

4 Can you see any links between products from different manufacturers that appear to be in competition?

▲ *Street culture can become fashionable.*

Television link: *Tectactics* – Recycling Waste

27 Designing for recycling

More and more, designers have to keep recycling in mind when they are developing new products

▲ *People are encouraged to recycle when they are doing their shopping.*

Pads of paper, supermarket bags and packaging are now labelled as environmentally friendly because they are made from **recycled** paper or plastics. Recycled means that the material has already been used to make something else. When the useful life of the original product was over, the materials in it were used to make a new product. Recycling is now very important.

At your local supermarket there may be containers or 'banks' for glass, cans, paper, and even rags. This waste is taken away to recycling centres where it is broken down to reusable raw materials.

Pause for thought
Stop and think about all the materials that get thrown away in your home.

The world as a rubbish tip?

Most household rubbish is made up of waste food and discarded packaging. It is taken by waste contractors to **landfill sites** where it is buried in deep holes. In the past this process has been used to reclaim land which has been mined or quarried. This improves the environment. However, it is not always possible to find landfill sites and other methods have to be used. Sometimes waste materials are burned but this can cause air pollution.

▲ *This site is built on a landfill.*

It is not just kitchen waste that ends up on the rubbish tip. Think about the number of scrap-yards you see piled high with rusty cars, or the local rubbish tip with its old cookers, vacuum cleaners and refrigerators. If the materials in these products could be recycled, we would be able to cut down on our use of raw materials.

Pause for thought
How do people dispose of big things like fridges, furniture and cars when they wear out?

Built to last?

Some people argue that if products lasted a really long time – perhaps forever – then we would use less raw materials. But this is not a sensible solution.

▲ *Lasts longer but not forever.*

Imagine if there was a light bulb that lasted forever. Who would make it? In the end, they would put themselves out of business. In fact, just such a light bulb is supposed to have been invented! The patent for the invention was quietly bought by a major light bulb producer but they did not go ahead with its manufacture. They bought the patent to prevent this light bulb ever being manufactured and sold.

▲ *Old refrigerators create special disposal problems because they often contain gases called CFCs which can damage the environment.*

Designing for recycling

One way forward is for products to last for a reasonable length of time and to be made of materials that can be recycled easily once the product's useful life is over. Designers and engineers have a key role to play in this. Instead of designing products that wear out and are thrown away, they need to develop products that can be recycled – *to design for recycling*. These products may also use recycled materials.

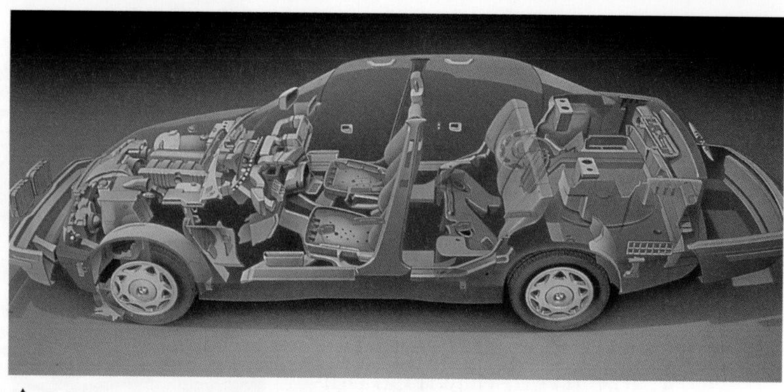

▲ *This car has been designed for recycling at specially built recycling plants.*

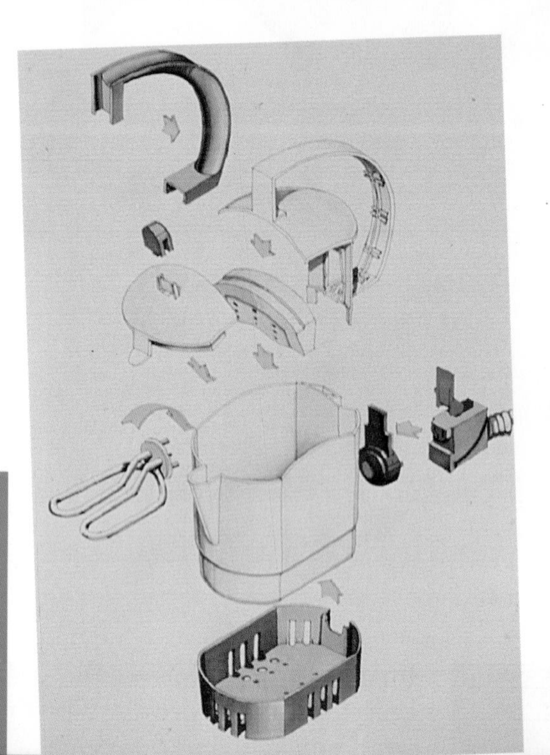

However large or small the product, the designer needs to consider:

- how it will be made;
- how it will be used;
- how it will be disposed of.

The designer can specify recyclable materials for the product. This may also affect how the product is made.

If something is going to be recycled easily and cost-effectively it will need to:

- be easy to take to pieces to get to the bits that can be recycled;
- be made from as few parts as possible;
- ideally, have those parts that are suitable for recycling clearly marked or coded with information about the material and a 'recyclable' symbol.

Will anyone bother?

Is anyone going to go to all this trouble? Some manufacturers are already beginning to move in this direction. Here are two examples.

- BMW, the car manufacturer, has started an international recycling programme. This involves recycling centres, which break the used cars down into parts that can be recycled for their materials.
- Great British Kettles has designed and produced a kettle with component parts which snap together for quick assembly and quick disassembly. The parts are labelled for ease of recycling.

▲ *The materials in this kettle can be easily recycled.*

Research

How are materials recycled in your area? Draw up a list of methods and give each one a rating on a 3-point scale for how easy it is to use: 1 point for difficult to use to 3 points for easy to use. Why is it important for recycling methods to be easy to use?

28 Designing for energy conservation

Designers and engineers have very important parts to play in developing alternative, and more environmentally friendly, sources of energy

Not on my doorstep

When you turn on the television, CD player or even the bedside lamp, do you think about the source of energy and how that energy reaches your home or school? We all take for granted an endless supply of energy, always available at the flick of a switch.

Only a small percentage of the country's population have to put up with coal-fields or a power station near their town or village. These are the sources of the energy that we all take for granted. The rest of us can 'turn a blind eye' and be thankful that they are not on our doorsteps. But public opinion is changing about our environment and more effort is being made to repair the damage caused by our endless demands for energy.

▲ *Using fossil fuels has spoiled the environment in the past.*

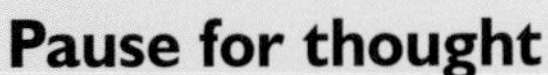

Pause for thought

Communities around the world have developed rapidly during this century. Many new inventions make life easier. Could people be persuaded to give up some of these to cut down on the demands for energy?

▲ *You can't see the gas pipelines but they are there!*

Using the wind

Windmills were first recorded as being used in the tenth century, one thousand years ago. They harnessed the energy of the wind to operate simple machines, particularly millstones for grinding wheat for flour.

Modern wind turbines are much more powerful. They convert wind energy into electrical energy. Some countries already make considerable use of wind energy. North America has more than three million wind generators, providing about 300 million kWh a year! In the 1970s, North America developed the most powerful wind engine, producing more than 2 MW of power. Holland began developing a wind farm in 1986, with 25 wind engines, designed to supply a town of 10 000 people with all its energy needs.

◀ *Old and new technologies for harnessing wind energy.* ▲

Both countries recognized that they need to preserve their dwindling fossil fuel reserves. By investing money in research and development they overcame three major problems associated with wind energy.

1 Finding suitable sites

The weather in a country has to be thoroughly investigated to find sites where:

- the wind blows throughout the year;
- the wind blows hard enough to generate power but not so hard that it destroys the windmills.

2 The way the wind blows

The wind does not blow steadily or in the same direction, even on windy sites, so the windmills have to be designed to produce constant output power from changing input power.

▲ *This wind farm is far away from where people live, but some people think it spoils the environment.*

3 Protecting the environment

Suitable sites for wind farms are often in remote areas where they have least effect on people. However, such sites may be of great natural beauty and support a variety of living things. The wind farm design must not damage or spoil the site.

1 Draw a quick sketch of a modern windmill. Add notes to describe:

a the requirements for the site;

b the power output from the windmill.

2 Work in a group of four. Imagine that a company wants to build a wind farm in your area. Several local groups are opposed to the idea because they think it will spoil the environment. Work out the arguments that you would use to convince these people that it would be a good idea.

▲ *Wind-powered fossil fuel transport!*

The Japanese have developed an interesting use for wind power. They launched the first wind-powered petrol tanker in 1980. Although it transports fossil fuel products, it is powered by harnessing the wind!

Research

1 Find out how the wind blows in your area:

a Is there a prevailing wind direction? If so what is it?
b How many windy days are there in a year?
c How many completely calm days are there in a year?
d What has been the highest wind speed over the past ten years?

You may wish to talk to your geography teacher about this.

2 Use the answers to these questions to decide whether it is worth looking for a wind farm site in your area.

What about our buildings?

Architects have an important role to play in the design of energy-saving homes and offices. Energy is used least effectively in our homes. Energy is wasted through bad insulation of pipes, walls, lofts and poorly fitting windows. This is one of the easiest areas in which we can all conserve energy – and save money on fuel bills at the same time.

▲ *The new students' residential block at the University of East Anglia, in Norwich, is energy efficient as it recycles heat.*

29 Predicting is important

Predicting is important both in the natural world and in marketing

Predicting the natural world

Natural phenomena such as volcanoes, earthquakes, tornadoes and typhoons cause tremendous damage. It is important to be able to predict when and where they will happen to save lives. Volcanoes present a special problem as it is very difficult to predict where molten lava will come out of the mountainside.

One area of prediction that we all take for granted is the weather. Weather reports are given out every day, almost hourly, on television and radio, and daily in newspapers. Usually they are very accurate.

Weather changes are so important to farmers that the Ministry of Agriculture, Fisheries and Food makes sure that they can get long-range weather forecasts easily. This helps them to judge the best time to harvest their crops to make sure they are of a high quality for the food manufacturers and customers.

The sales of products such as ice-cream and umbrellas depend on the weather. Their sellers need weather forecasts far enough in advance to prepare and organize their stock. Accurate prediction is crucial to their livelihoods.

▲ *Natural forces are very strong and can cause disasters.*

Pause for thought
How do we collect the information we need to predict changes in the weather, earthquakes and volcanic eruptions?

Weather forecasts

In the past **meteorologists** (scientists who study the weather) used barometers to measure changes in air pressure as an important means of weather forecasting. Today we use space technology. The geostationary satellite, METEOSAT-4, is used for weather forecasting all around the world. Many kilometres up in space, it continually circles the Earth, scanning changes in the weather. It can detect a gathering storm and track its journey. Meteorologists use this information, and special computer software, to predict where, say, a typhoon is going to arrive. This gives people time to move and protect their homes and belongings as best they can.

▲ *Old and new ways of measuring pressure to forecast weather conditions.*

Volcanic eruptions

Scientists use two methods for predicting when volcanoes might erupt:

- One method involves analysing gases given off by the volcano. The exact content of these gases changes just before the volcano erupts.
- The other method involves measuring carefully the size and shape of the volcano. Volcanoes swell up before an eruption. Using a computer-assisted measuring system scientists were able to measure a 1 mm increase in the size of the volcanic crater on Sakurajima Island, Japan. This enabled them to predict accurately the 1985 eruption.

▲ *METEOSAT-4 provides information for the world's weather forecasters.*

▲ *The volcanic eruption on Sakurajima Island, Japan in 1985.*

Earthquakes

Minor movements in the Earth's crust usually come before major earthquakes. The study of these movements is called **seismology**. Seismologists can use lasers or especially sensitive optical-fibre devices to detect the tiniest movements in the Earth's crust. By studying these movements, they try to predict where and when earthquakes might occur and how serious they will be. They do not yet know enough to get it right all the time and damaging earthquakes can still occur without warning in populated areas.

▲ *This earthquake in Armenia in 1988 was not predicted and many people were killed.*

Pause for thought

Why do people live in areas where they know there will be earthquakes, typhoons and volcanic eruptions?

Designing to minimize disaster

Many people live in places where natural disasters, such as earthquakes, typhoons and volcanic eruptions occur. Fortunately these disasters do not happen very often so most of the time it is quite safe. But, when they do happen, many people can lose their homes and lives. Predicting such disasters allows the population to leave before it becomes dangerous, but buildings, roads and bridges still suffer.

Architects and engineers are working together to develop designs for buildings and other structures that will withstand natural disasters so that any damage is minimized and life can return to normal very quickly once the danger is over. This work involves developing new materials and new construction techniques. Small-scale tests are carried out in laboratories along with a lot of computer modelling before large-scale test buildings are constructed. The findings are used to make recommendations to the building industry and result in new standards for buildings.

▲ *This skyscraper in Hong Kong has been designed to withstand earthquakes.*

Research

Find out where in the world there have been major earthquakes over the past 50 years and mark the places on a map. Can you see a pattern?

Predicting in the market-place

A company launches a new product because it has predicted there is a market for that product. This market depends on many factors. Some are in the control of the company, such as:

- good advertising which lets people know that the product exists;
- good distribution so that the product is in the shops and can be bought.

▲ *Someone has predicted that these goods will sell.*

Other factors are under the control of competing companies, such as:

- advertising that promotes a rival product.

Some forces are outside the control of those trying to sell their goods:

- price of raw materials, for example, which often depends on decisions made by governments in foreign countries.

▲ *The forecasters knew about this a long time before you did.*

For fashion and textiles, forecasting takes on a different meaning. Years before fashion garments are on sale in shops or appear in magazines, fashion forecasters develop forecasts of looks, colours, garment shapes and overall trends for the coming seasons. These ideas are assembled on boards and presented to clients or published in the fashion and textile forecasting magazines.

Designers of fashion clothes and fabrics use these forecasts for research or as background information to support their own ideas. The fashion industry generally works two to three seasons ahead of the products on sale in the shops, but forecasting agencies are often working four to five seasons ahead, and sometimes more!

Research

Collect some pictures showing record players over the past 70 years. Arrange them in a time-line and label each one with its date. Can you see any trend in their appearance? Can you work out how the next style of record player will look?

30 Warning lights

Light has been used to warn of danger since early times. In the days when even candle-light was a luxury, the blaze of beacons could be seen for many kilometres. No other form of lighting could compete with these beacons

Pause for thought

What might ancient people have needed warning about? What other ways could they have used to provide a warning?

Lighthouses have shown warning lights for more than 2000 years. The Pharos at Alexandria in Egypt was probably the first lighthouse. One of the 'seven wonders of the world', it was built in about 300 BC. It is said to have stood over 120 metres tall.

Mirrors were used to send light from a giant fire to ships far out at sea. This light probably helped guide ships back to the port, though lighthouses usually act as a warning of dangers close by.

Research

Against what dangers do lighthouses warn approaching ships? Find out all you can about the role of today's lighthouses and the technology used to make them work successfully.

From candle power to electricity

The modern lighthouse owes its existence to a British engineer, Henry Winstanley. He built a lighthouse on the dangerous Eddystone Rock in the English Channel, 22 kilometres from Plymouth, Devon. It took two years to build and came into operation in 1698, burning 60 candles!

It must have been quite a job to light all the candles, and to make sure they continued to shine all night and during fog. This lighthouse worked for only five years before a storm swept it away in 1703 (with its inventor inside!).

Pause for thought

Think about the number of candles needed in this lighthouse, and the difficulty in building the structure in the first place. What does this tell you about the need for a lighthouse at Eddystone?

When electric arc lights were invented, and lenses were used to focus the light into a beam, lighthouses became more reliable and easier to see.

Research

In what other situations has the invention of the electric light been a major influence?

On the road

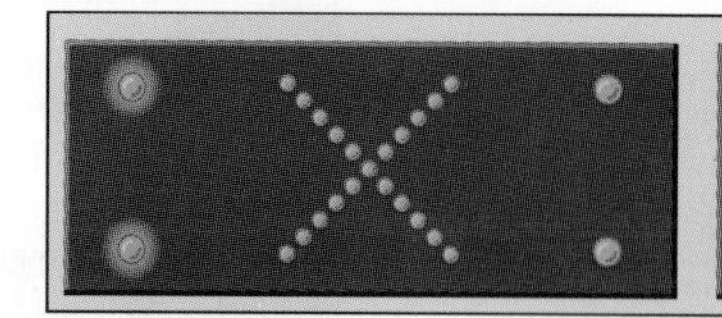
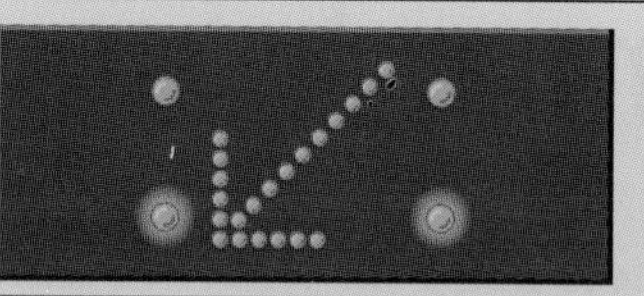
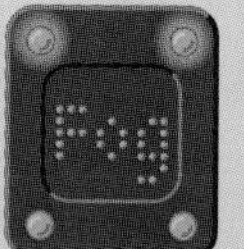

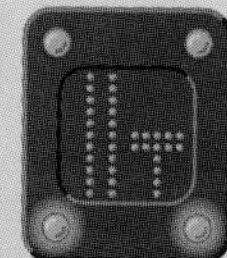

The flashing light is a familiar warning sign on our roads. It is used in different ways:

- Emergency vehicles use flashing lights as well as sirens to let us know they are there.
- Hazard lights on vehicles flash to warn us that they may be dangerous.
- Motorway signs flash to warn of danger or speed restrictions.
- The lights at a railway crossing flash to warn us that a train is coming.
- The flashing yellow light on the side of a rubbish skip warns us it is there.
- Indicator lights on cars let us know that the driver intends to pull out or turn.

1 What forms of warning were there before flashing lights became available?

2 What is it about a flashing light that makes it so useful as a warning sign?

3 What are the best colours to signal danger? What makes them so effective?

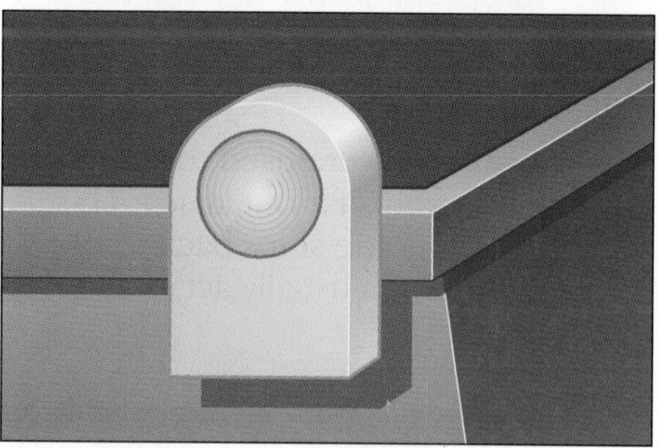

4 In what other situations are coloured lights used to give warnings?

Traffic lights

Traffic lights use a 'code' of colours to warn us when to stop and go at road junctions.

The world's first traffic lights were installed near the House of Commons in London in1868. The red and green gas lights were set in a revolving lantern, on top of a cast-iron pillar about 7 metres high. One night in 1869 the gas exploded, injuring the policeman who was operating the lights.

Despite this accident, the lights were used for the convenience of Members of Parliament until 1872. It was not until 1926 that traffic lights reappeared in London.

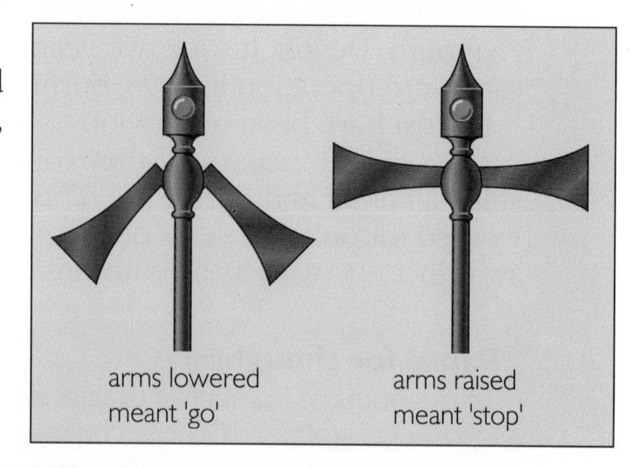

Research
Test some different coloured lights (using a simple light bulb and filter set-up) to see which colour is most highly visible. Try out the different colours in various conditions – daylight, dim lighting, darkness, street lighting, and so on.

31 Maps and guides

The way maps and guides are made is changing due to advances in technology. Our changing needs have also demanded new ways of making maps.

When we visit a town, a theme park, an ancient monument or even another school, a map or guide can often help us find our way around. We sometimes take it for granted that if we want to find out about a place we will be able to find a map or guide to give us the information.

▲ *These maps and guides are for the same area, but each is presented differently and focuses on different things.*

Pause for thought
Why do we use maps? How do you think we would manage without them?

1. Why is each product in the photograph different?
2. How do you think each would be used?
3. Who might use each map or guide?

Research
Find as many examples as you can of guides and maps describing your local area. Compare the different styles of presentation.

We often need to describe an area or place with a diagram. The diagram needs to be drawn carefully so that the information on it is clear *and* complete. The **scale** is an important part of the diagram. It tells you the distances between the various features in the diagram, and how big an area it covers.

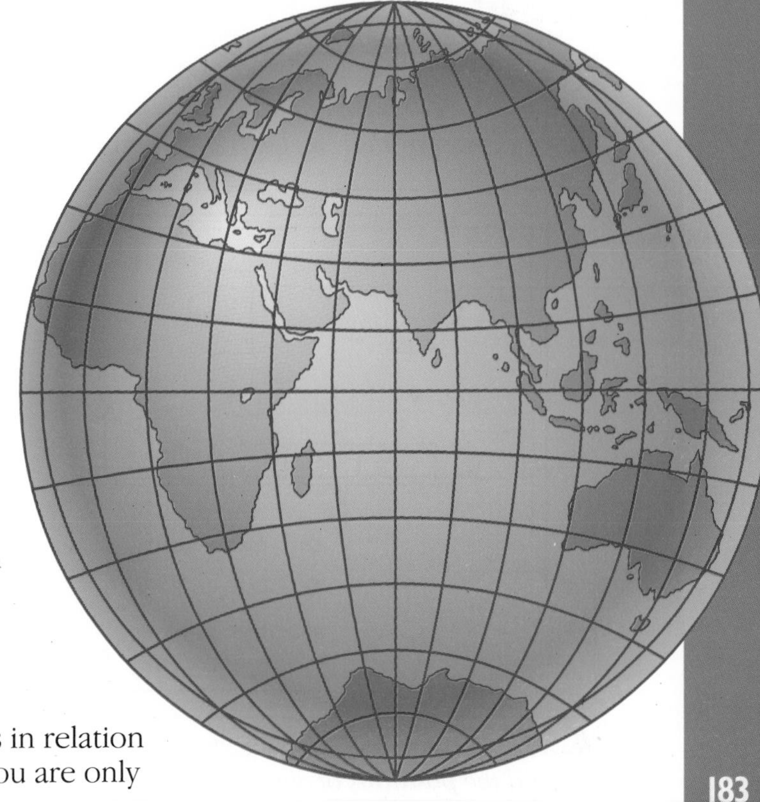

A matter of detail

A global map shows the position of countries in relation to one another, but it will not help much if you are only planning a short journey.

A map can use graphics to show the positions of places in relation to one another. It might be able to show you the character of the area as well.

A street map uses graphics to show the location of features such as roads, rivers and buildings.

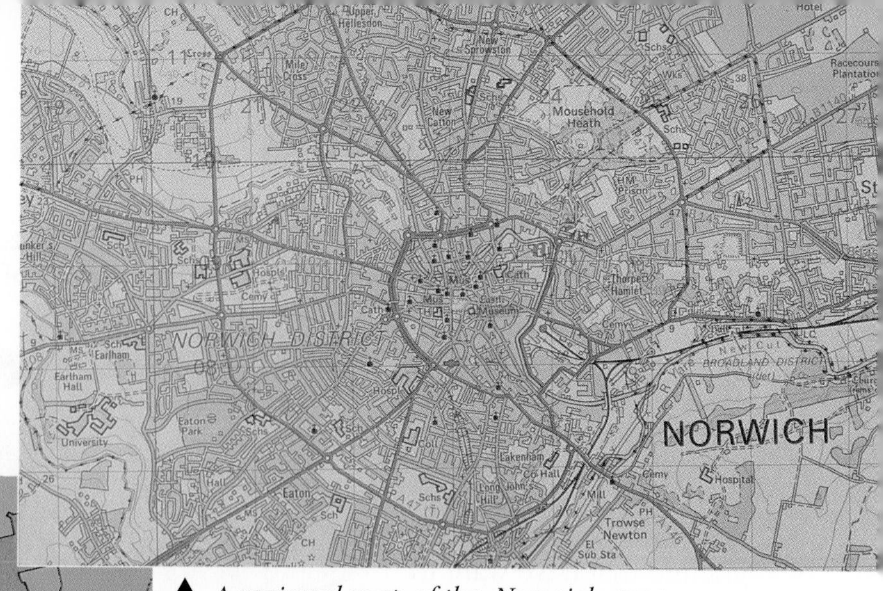

▲ *A regional map of the Norwich area.*

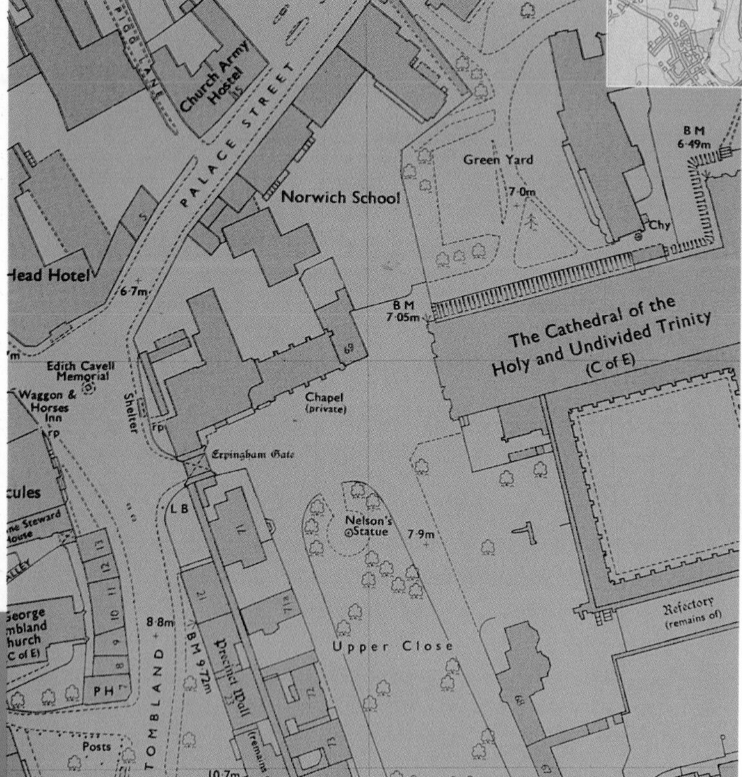

▲ *An extract from a Norwich street map.*

1 When would the street map be more useful than the regional map?

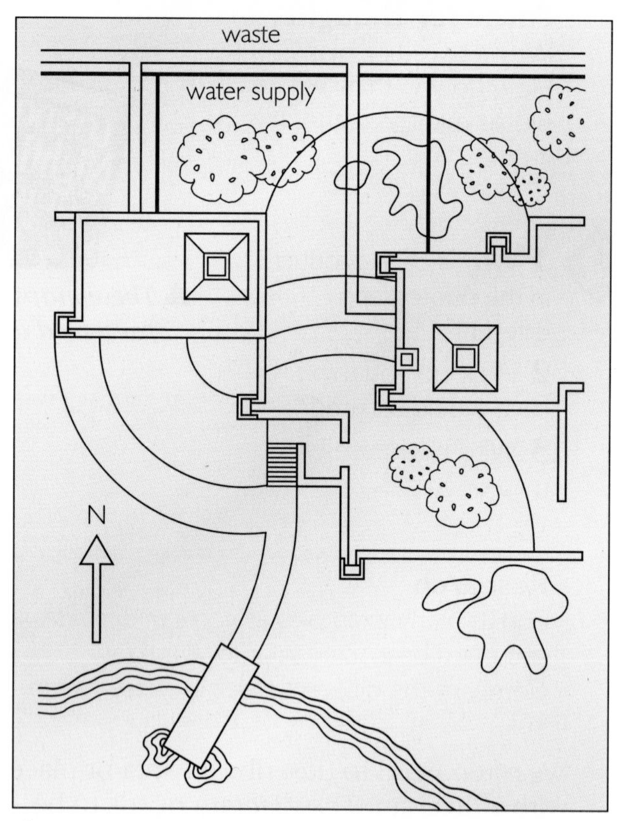

▲ *A site plan uses graphics to show the layout and location of features such as buildings, pipes, cables and trees.*

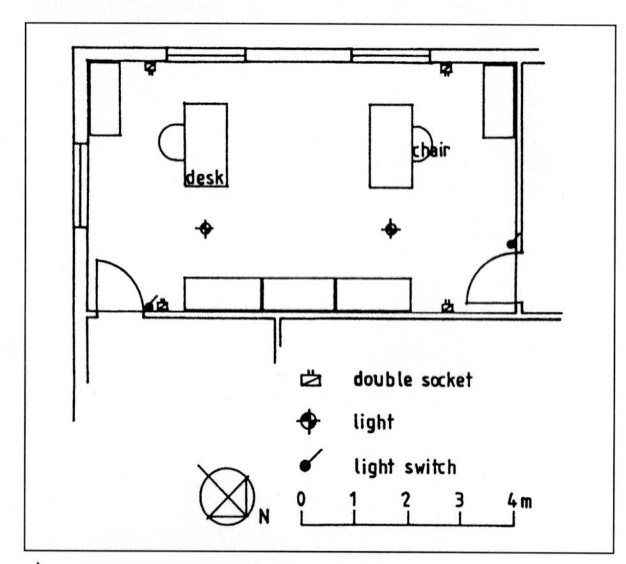

▲ *A room plan can show the shape of an area and the positions of objects such as furniture.*

All these maps and plans show the information as a 'bird's eye view'. This means they show what an area looks like when viewed from above.

2 What are the advantages of presenting information as a bird's eye or plan view?

People have drawn maps of their environment for centuries. The oldest known map is a small clay tablet from Babylon, made in about 2300 BC. At that time people had no signposts to guide them, but a map of their surroundings enabled them to find their way from one settlement to another. These rough maps used pictures of landmarks such as rivers, large trees, rocks and woodland.

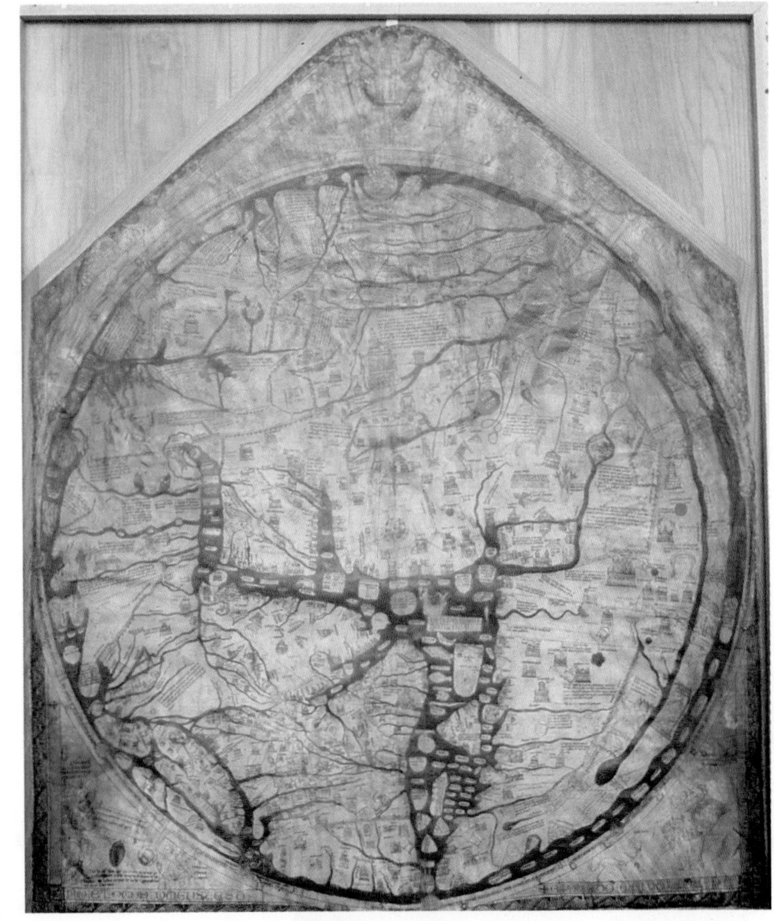

▲ *The* Mappa Mundi, *one of the oldest known maps of the world, was drawn around 1300 by a canon at Hereford Cathedral, England.*

> **Pause for thought**
> How could people have collected, sorted and kept the information for this kind of map? If there was no map of an area, how else could travellers have found their way?

In Britain, the Ordnance Survey was set up in 1791. This marked the start of more organized and accurate map-making. The threat of invasion from France led to the British Army's demand for more detailed maps of the southern coast of England. Using land-surveying techniques, the first one-inch to one-mile map of Kent was produced in 1801.

The invention of the hot-air balloon in the 1780s was an important step forward in map-making. For the first time a *real* bird's eye view of the land could be seen. By the time powered aircraft came along in the early 1900s, aerial photography was already being used to help chart the landscape.

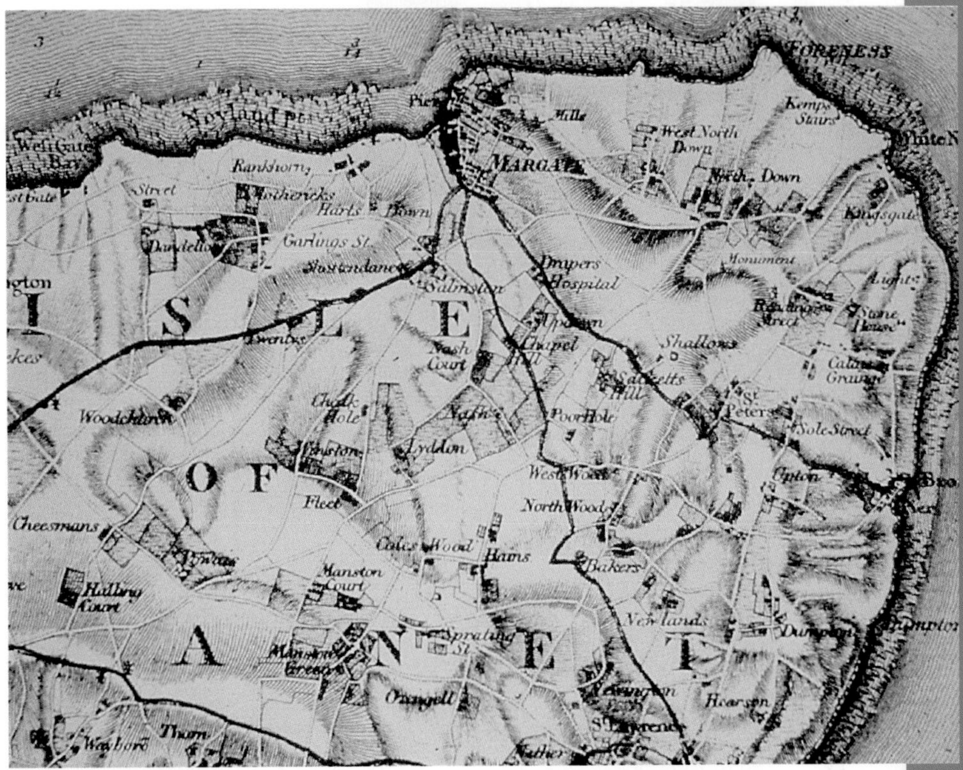

▲ *An extract from the first Ordnance Survey map of Kent.*

In recent years, map-making has benefited from our increased technological skills. The use of satellite photographs has meant that more accurate maps of large areas can be produced. Surveys from the air are now common, and as a result vast areas of uninhabited parts of the world have now been mapped.

1 What changes in the way people live would drive them to produce more accurate maps?

Producing a map or guide is not as straightforward as it might seem. The first challenge is collecting the information. Sorting all the data is the next problem. Finally, you need to decide how the information is going to be presented.

The first Ordnance Survey maps were printed in black and white. Now full-colour maps are available on CD-ROMs, together with aerial photographs, ground level photographs, text, graphs and statistics. The maps and photographs are on different scales so that it is possible to zoom in on an area.

Sometimes you may want the information on a map or guide to make it visually exciting and interesting, as well as easy to understand. That's when the creative use of graphics is important.

One of the most famous examples of the use of graphics is the London Underground map. It is a clear and easily understandable guide to a complicated system, but it does not represent the true geography of the places or train lines it shows.

Research

Compare the London Underground map with a street guide to London. What would the Underground map look like if it followed the street plan exactly?

32 Food mixers

Food mixers and processors have been developed to meet new needs. Design and technology have made the task easier

In Britain we are used to a varied diet. Most of us expect to eat meals that are the result of mixing, blending or combining different ingredients.

Many different products are available for processing food, and it seems that a kitchen is not complete without a food mixer or blender.

Why mix food?

In her famous book, Mrs Beeton described the development of cookery as a mark of society's progress. Primitive people had a very dull diet – roots and berries made up much of the available food. People began to look for ways of varying their diet.

First, hunting and fishing provided some variety. Then, agricultural skills were developed: sowing and reaping crops, and breeding animals.

Soon, the aim was no longer simply to survive and live, but to live well. At this point the art of cookery was born. The raw materials remained much the same – fruit, vegetables, meat and fish – but they were improved, mixed and prepared with skill to create new foods for people to enjoy.

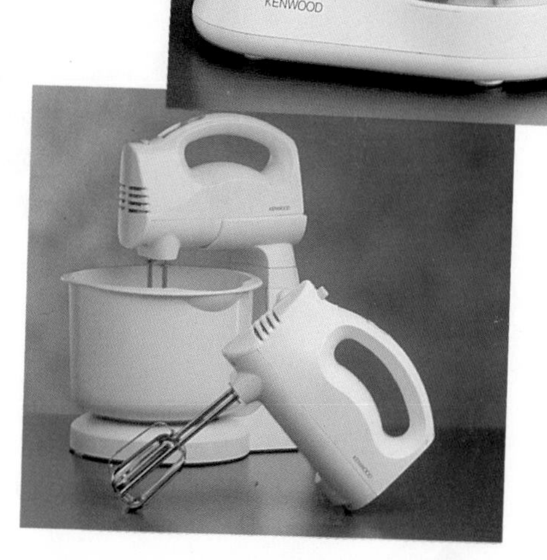

▲ *This range of mixers, blenders and processors is produced by just one company.*

▲ *Designing a machine that can process all these different foods is a challenge.*

Research

List all the foods that you eat in one day or a week which involve the use of a food mixer. Look in recipe books if necessary.

What are the tasks?

Food preparation has always involved many small tasks. These include:

- cutting and chopping (vegetables and meat);
- beating (eggs and batters);
- kneading (dough);
- grinding (spices and coffee);
- whisking (eggs, cream and milk);
- slicing (meat).

For centuries, the tools and equipment to perform these tasks remained fairly basic, mostly hand-made and hand-powered. At the beginning of the nineteenth century many elaborate machines were developed to save labour. However, it often took longer to set the machines up than to do the task by hand!

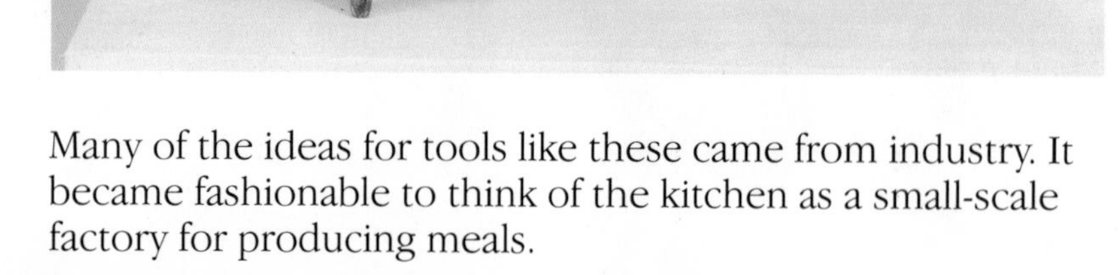

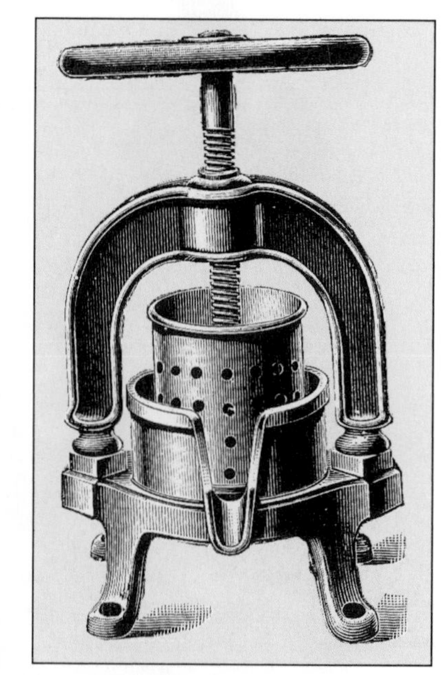

Many of the ideas for tools like these came from industry. It became fashionable to think of the kitchen as a small-scale factory for producing meals.

1 What do you think the tools in the pictures were used for?

2 Ask yourself these questions to find out how they work:

- Where would the user hold the tool?
- What would they do with the part that they hold?
- Does the food go in and come out? If so, where?
- Is the food held in place and worked on? If so where?
- Are there any mechanical parts? Can you see what they do?
- Can you see how the tool is held onto the table?

Pause for thought
How often do you eat foods that require no preparation? Why are so many foods processed and not left in their natural state? What do you think food used to be like before food processing?

A design classic

The hand-operated 'egg-beater' mixer was patented in 1873. With its revolving beaters, it was almost the same as the whisk we use today.

The mechanism is clearly visible and it is a good example of gearing in action. The gears speed up the action of moving blades through the food mixture, and the blades or whisks move in opposite directions to increase the rate of movement even more.

3 In 1873, the whisk was made from a mixture of cast iron and pressed iron sheet with tinned blades. What materials do you think the modern version is made from?

4 How do you think whisking was carried out before the mixer was developed?

5 Why is this product still in use today?

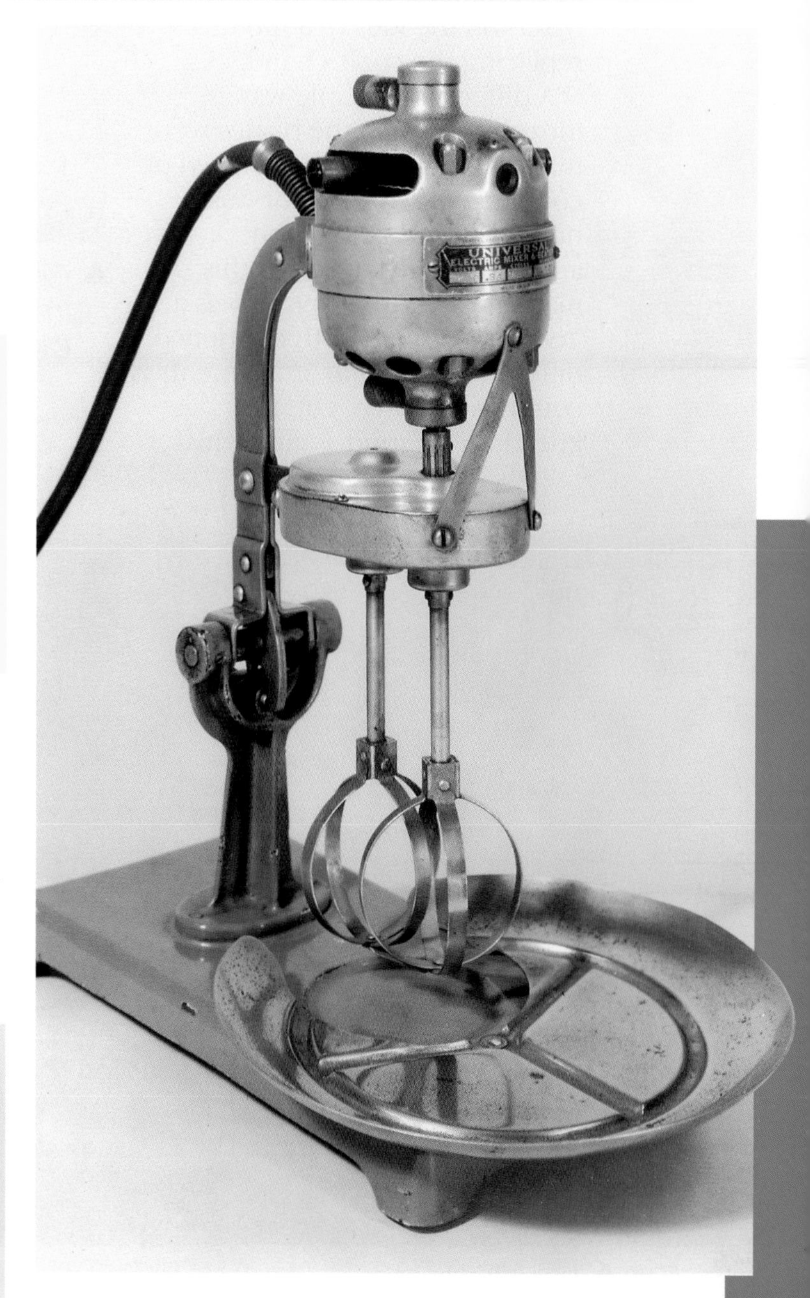

Electric motors

The widespread use of electricity and the development of the electric motor were key factors in the development of kitchen gadgets. When electric motors became small and reliable enough, the obvious next step was to motorize the whisk.

Pause for thought
The 'portable' electric food mixer shown opposite, introduced in 1918, was the first electric mixer designed for home use. What sort of appliances might have used the bigger, bulkier electric motors that were available 30 year before?

The kitchen machine

The shape and design of the early electric food mixers were inspired by industrial machines. It is easy to see their origins in tools like the drill.

Later models could be detached from their bases and used as portable units. Next, different attachments enabled the appliance to do other tasks like kneading and shredding. All these developments in design were based on the idea of a motor replacing the cook's hand.

A different principle was introduced when the blades were made to rotate within the bowl or container and the motor was housed in the base of the appliance. No longer was this machine a 'food mixer', it was a 'food processor'. With a variety of different blades and attachments it could juice, shred, cut, beat, knead, slice, grind … and whisk.

▲ *Food processing from 1920 to today.* ▼

▲ *This multi-purpose machine can be used to do most of the food preparation in our kitchens.*

Q

6 Food processor manufacturers also produce simpler, single-purpose tools. What do you think is the reason for this?

7 How has the development of the food mixer been influenced by our changing diet and eating habits?

33 Netting

Nets are often associated with fishing where they are used to catch fish. They are constructed from an open-meshed fabric so that the water runs out and the fish are held in the net. In fishing a wide range of netting is used

Pause for thought
Why do you think the size of the mesh is important?

Netting is used in tea-strainers and hair-nets, in personal survival nets and bags for nuts. What is it, and why do we use it?

Netting is an open-meshed material twisted, woven, knotted or welded together at regular intervals. It can be made from natural or synthetic material, it can be hand knitted or machine knitted. The mesh can vary in size from microscopic to centimetres wide, depending on its use.

Knitting is a form of netting. ▶

Pause for thought
Look at the picture showing work on a building site. It includes many examples of the use of netting. Why is netting used rather than another material?

▲ *Netting is widely used on building sites.*

▲ *A 'hard' net.*

Research
The netting used on a building site must be very strong and hard-wearing. Each knot or join must be strong. Look at the knots or joins used in sports netting in your school. What are the knots like? What material is the netting made from?

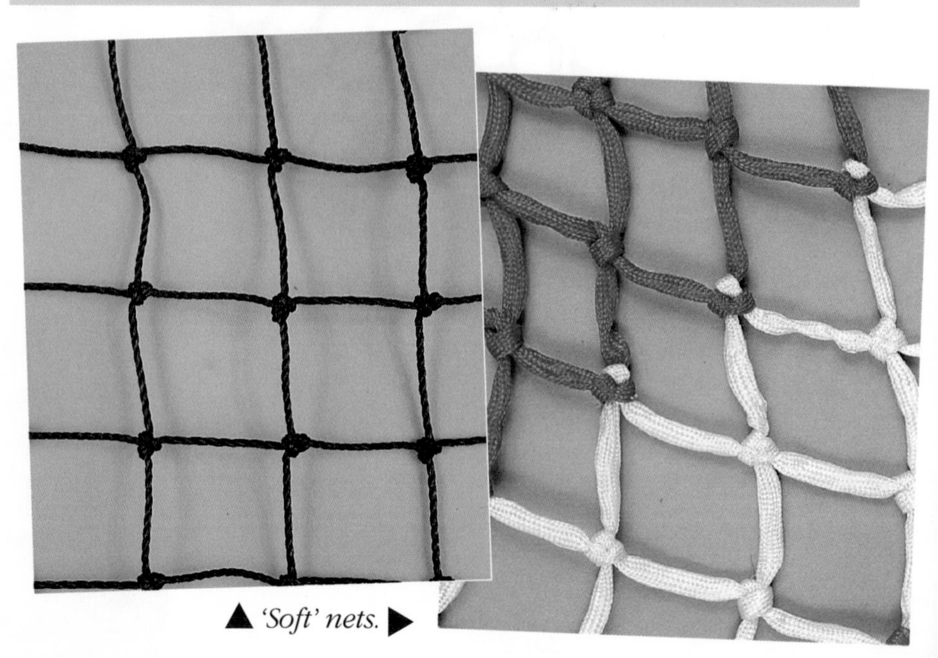

▲ *'Soft' nets.* ▶

1 Supermarkets use netting a lot. When Kim was researching netting she produced an alphabetical list of its uses. Can you add anything to Kim's A-Z of Netting?

2 Do you think she got anything wrong? If so, explain why.

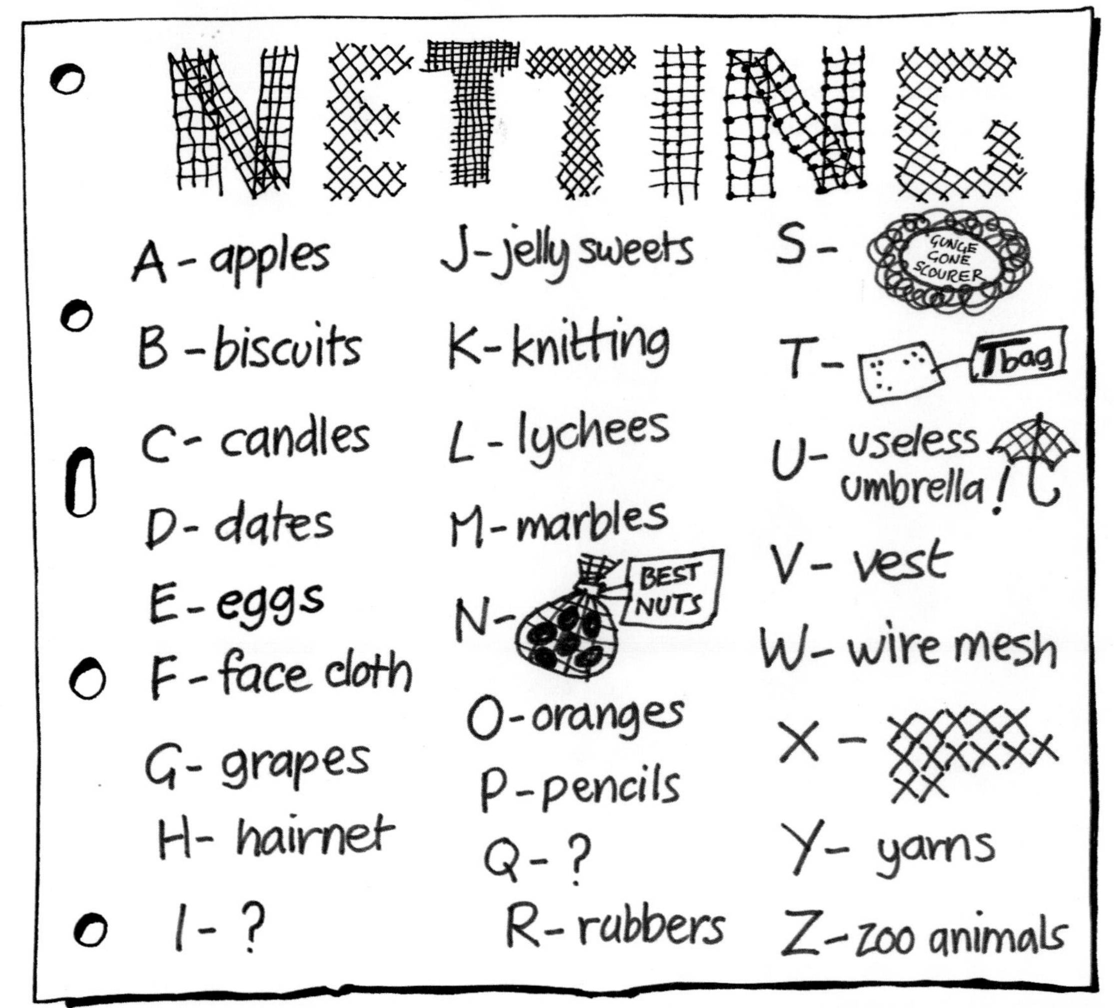

3 Consider the advantages and disadvantages of enclosing food products in netting or thin sheet materials. Are they both:

- eco-friendly?
- reusable?
- recyclable?
- porous (able to absorb water, air or other fluids)?
- visible?
- attractive?
- cheap?
- waterproof?

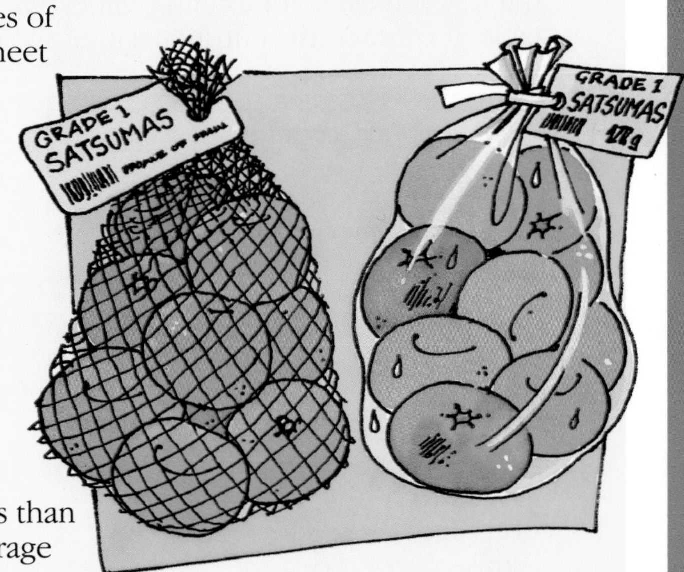

4 Do you think netting has more advantages than thin sheeting? If it has, how could we encourage its use?

34 Pop Tarts

Pop Tarts are a sweet snack, sold in most supermarkets. They come wrapped in foil, six to a box. They are designed to be heated in a toaster and eaten warm. If you could cross toast and jam with a square jam tart, you might arrive at a Pop Tart

▲ *Snack foods can be eaten instead of a traditional meal.*

Do you enjoy snack foods? What do you like? Are they sweet or savoury? Do you prepare them or are they ready-made? When do you eat them? Do you buy them? How much do they cost?

Q

1 Pop Tarts are a new idea in snacks. What do you think the manufacturers based this idea on?
2 Why are they wrapped in foil?
3 Is the name a good one? Why?

When is a snack not a snack?

How big or small does food have to be to still be a snack? Is it the way you eat it, for example with your fingers? Look at this table. It contains the nutritional information for one Pop Tart.

One Pop Tart contains:

Energy	210 Kcals
Protein	3 g
Carbohydrate	35 g
Fat	6 g
Fibre	0.7 g
Sodium	0. 25 g
Plus vitamins	

Pause for thought

Do you ever have a snack *meal*? When and what is it?

Research

Find out the same information for a snack of your choice.

Pop Tarts are made of two layers of pastry sandwiched together with a fruit or chocolate filling. They are rectangular with sealed edges. They are advertised as a 'delicious, anytime snack'.

Susie wrote this about them. Do you agree with her?

Pop Tarts could be described as a development of a toast and jam snack. Steven compared a Pop Tart with toast and a jam tart. He looked at appearance, feel in the mouth, aroma, flavour and how it was made.

Product	Pop Tart	Toast and jam	Jam tart
What does it look like?	A large pale biscuit	A brown square with shiny red stuff on it	Small, round and shiny in the middle
The smell	Fruit cake	Hot bread	No smell
In the mouth	Crispy and then squidgy	Crunchy and then soggy	Hard and then soft and sticky
The taste	Very sweet quickly	Sweet and buttery	Very sweet and fruity
How is it made?	In a factory, by machine. I toasted it.	I made it	In a factory and I don't think the jam is cooked
Is it a good snack?	Two Pop Tarts would be good for breakfast as they're quick.	Yes, if I was hungry	If you want a small snack
What else is good about it?	They keep a long time.	It is made from things you usually have in the cupboard	If you weren't really hungry.

4 Why are Pop Tarts made of pastry rather than bread?

5 Do you agree with Steven's comments? Would you add anything to the chart, or change anything in it?

35 Taking cover

The resources of design and technology have been used to provide better forms of protection for the head and face

Although the human body offers its own defence against many forms of attack, there are numerous dangers that can prove harmful or even lethal. Our skin can protect our inner organs to some extent, but when faced, for example, with excess heat, extreme cold, flying objects, radiation or chemicals, we need added protection.

People have always recognised such dangers and have tried to protect themselves. In the past armour was used for protection in warfare. From just a helmet and leg guards in Bronze Age Greece, this developed into full body armour in sixteenth century Europe.

1 Look at the suit of armour shown here. Why do you think it stopped being used?

2 What took its place?

Research

The pictures show examples of helmets from different periods in history. Find out how head protection has changed over the centuries. What are the differences in the materials used? Collect pictures to show the differences between periods.

The face is a specially sensitive area. We depend on our eyes, in particular, for information about our surroundings, so it is hardly surprising that much attention has been paid to protecting the face.

Sporting lives

Sport is sometimes described as a modern form of warfare. This certainly seems true judging by the protective clothing now worn in some sports! Protective headgear is becoming more and more common for people taking part in high-risk sports.

New materials have been developed so that lighter but stronger headgear can be made. These improve the protection available to cricketers, hockey players and American footballers, among others. They are all designed to offer protection against fast-moving objects.

▲ *An American football player wears padding and a crash helmet for protection against impact.*

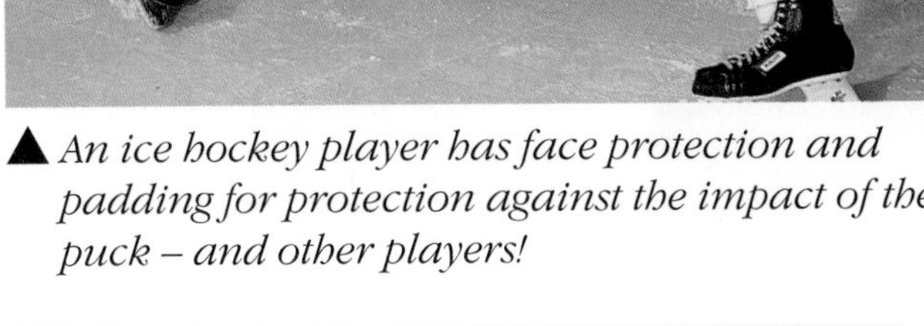

▲ *An ice hockey player has face protection and padding for protection against the impact of the puck – and other players!*

▲ *A cricketer wears face, body and leg protection against the impact of a very hard ball and fast bowling.*

3 Look at these photographs. How have they tried to solve the problem of protection?

4 Why are the solutions different?

5 Why do you think that this form of face protection is more common nowadays that it used to be?

Sometimes it is necessary to provide the face and eyes with protection from other hazards. Swimmers and divers need to protect their eyes from the water, and so a different form of mask is required.

7 The goggles used by the jockey in the picture are designed to protect against two hazards. What do you think they are?

Fashion

Sunglasses are useful for protecting the eyes against the Sun's ultraviolet rays, but they are also a way of projecting an image. They can also be used to protect your identity or privacy.

▲ *Sunglasses for protection, privacy and style.*

At work

Safety at work is very important. Much stress has been placed on protecting our face and eyes from possible injury. Methods range from wearing a pair of goggles to protect eyes from flying debris to wearing a complete hood and ventilation system to protect from dangerous chemicals or gases.

Standards

If the materials used to make a protective mask or headgear are not chosen carerfully, the risk of injury might actually be increased. It is no use making a visor to protect from flying debris if the plastic forming the shield is going to shatter if it is hit hard.

For this reason safety products like these should conform to a set of standards.These are often internationally agreed. They make sure that the products have been tested and will perform in a certain way under set conditions.

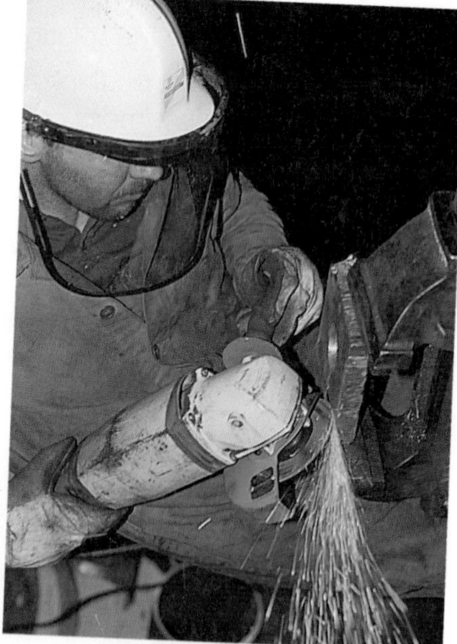

▲ *A clear plastic visor gives good visibility and protects from flying debris.*

▲ *A full-face mask protects the face and eyes from hot flying sparks and the blinding flash of the welding.*

▲ *A mask and a respirator for a firefighter protect against debris, gas, heat and smoke.*

Research

Find out the standards for a particular group of safety products, like protective goggles, ear protectors or dust masks.

Index

P

Q

R

S

T

Acknowledgements

We are grateful to the following for permission to reproduce photographs and other copyright material:
(A = above, B = below, L = left, R = right, C = centre, F = far)

Ace Photo Agency 101B (Alexis Sofianopoulos), 188A (Stuart Frawley), 191CR (Michael Bluestone), 196 (Kevin Phillips), 197AL (Benelux Press), 198AR (SP Productions), 198BC (Peter Adams); Allsport 163BR (David Cannon); Ancient Art & Architecture Collection 85, 86, 87B, 99A; Ardea 67 (Liz & Tony Bomford), 99C (Joanna Van Gruisen); BMW (GB) Ltd 172A; Barnaby's Picture Library 88B, 114BR, 115C, 170A, 174B, 177A; Gareth Boden 128, 131B, 135, 153B, 164A, 169B, 180A; Boots the Chemists Ltd 157; British Petroleum 173BL & BR; British Standards Institution 51R, 162B; J. Allan Cash 130, 162CR, 174A, 178C, 191A, 198BL & BR; Chris Coggins 89B; Colorific! 122(Action Plus), 152A (David Levenson), 162BC (Steve Benbow), 168BR (Raoul Benegas), 175B (Eiji Miyazawa/Black Star); Comstock 171A; Consumers' Association 51FR; Paddy Cutts 74, 75; Department of Trade & Industry & Central Office of Information 51C; C.M. Dixon 60, 87A; Duracell UK 165; E.T. Archive 114BC; Ecoscene 170B (Martin Jones); Mary Evans Picture Library 188BR; Express Lifts 118, 121; Fitch 172C & B; G.S.R. Innovations Ltd 125; Genesis Space Photo Library 178BR; Halfords 162BR; Robert Harding Picture Library 89A, 98R, 117C, 171B, 197BL (Bill Wood); Health Education Authority 73; The Dean & Chapter of Hereford & the Hereford Mappa Mundi Trustees 185A; Michael Holford 58, 78BR; Home Office & Central Office of Information 64A; Hotpoint 110; Jacqui Hurst 99B; Hutchison Library 178A; Richard Ingle 79, 80, 81, 82, 83; Intermediate Technology 76, 77, 92, 93, 102, 103, 104, 105, 126, 127, 128BL & BR, 129; *Just 17* 180B; Kenwood 187, 190BL; LFCDA 108, 109; Andrew Lambert 115BL; Levis Strauss (UK) Ltd 98L; Linwood Electronic 65A; London Transport Museum 186BR; Longman Photographic Unit 48, 51A & FL & L, 84, 100B, 134, 136, 137, 142A, 144, 145, 146, 149A, 159, 183, 186BL, 191B, 192, 194; Mansell Collection 88A; Rick Mather Architects 176; Mazda Lighting 171C; Metropolitan Police Service 65BR; Paul Mulcahy 160, 161; Museum of Costume & Textiles, Nottingham 138B; Museum of the Moving Image, London 78AR; National Trust Photographic Library 154A; Network 191CL (Peter Jordan); Northern Foods 148A; The Robert Opie Collection 158; © Crown Copyright, Ordnance Survey 184, 185B, 186A & C; Oxford Scientific Films 68 (Edward Parker); Philips Electronics UK Ltd 64C; from: *Pictorial History of Darvel*, James Mair, Alloway Publishing, 1989 140; from: *Pictorial History of Newmilns*, James Mair, Alloway Publishing, 1988 139; Popperfoto 114BL, 115R; Procter & Gamble 166; Product First 168A; Reflecting RoadStuds Ltd 150; Rex Features 70A (Andrew Dunsmore), 162CL, 153A (Robin Mayes), 168BCL (Dixon), 178BL (T. Nishiinoue); Rowan Yarns/Joey Toller 101AR; Rural History Centre, University of Reading 138A; Louise Rutherford 184BL; The Science Museum/Science & Society Picture Library 100A, 188BL & C, 189, 190A & BR; Science Photo Library 70B & 72 (St Bartholomew's Hospital), 71 (James King–Holmes); Scottish Lace Guild 142B, 143; Sony UK Ltd 164B; Spectrum Colour Library 154B; Tony Stone 162BL (Thomas Zimmermann), 163BL (Oli Tennent), 175A (Glen Allison), 177C (Paul Chesley), 177B (Robert Yager), 197C & BR; Sudanese Government/FAO 69; Syndication International 168BCR; TESCO 94B, 95, 96, 97A & C, 148B, 149C & B; TRIP 65BL & 97B & 114A & 117L & R (Helene Rogers), 116BL & 197AR(Eye Ubiquitous), 182 (Bob Turner), 198AL (G. Howe); Tedea–Huntleigh 116A; Telegraph Colour Library 162C (Chris Knapton), 163A (J. Taposchaner), 169A (Bavaria Bildagentur), 179B, 198AC (R. Lang); Shirley Thompson 64B; Topham Picturepoint 116BR, 152B, 168BL & 179A (Associated Press), 173A; Elizabeth Whiting Associates 156; York Archaeological Trust 78L.

We are grateful to the following for permission to reproduce copyright material:
Express Newspapers plc for headlines 'Blind man attacked as he exercises dog' & 'Thugs crush boy, 5, with tractor tyre' in *Daily Express* 21.04.94; Mirror Group Newspapers for headline 'Tragic playtime of little Caroline' in *Daily Mirror* 21.04.94; News Group Newspapers Ltd for headlines 'Dealer accused of £250m fake deals' in *The Sun* 20.04.94; 'Neighbour crippled tackling teen yobs' and 'Pals made perfect £20 notes on a photocopier' in *The Sun* 21.04.94; Times Newspapers Ltd for headline 'Gun Death trial hold of gentle victim' in *The Times* 21.04.94. © Times Newspapers Ltd, 1994.